*Give Father a Hard Knock*

# Give Father
# A Hard Knock

KEN KRAFT

Drawings by David Pascal

Doubleday & Company, Inc., Garden City, New York, 1962

Library of Congress Catalog Card Number 62–11455
Copyright © 1962 by Ken Kraft
All Rights Reserved
Printed in the United States of America
First Edition

This book is for John C. Flotte,
with gratitude and friendship,
and because he knew Father and Father's brood
and saved them many a hard knock.

# Foreword

Here in these pages is an expert on hard knocks—the senior Mr. Kraft. He is a man who made the shattering mistake of forgetting that children do grow up. This is an account of his traumatic experience as nominal head of a mutinous new household consisting of two sons almost as pigheaded as he, and a brand-new daughter-in-law full of bright ideas. Entering the scene a calm man who considered a family an uncomplex little group where Father was In Charge and enjoyed the admiration and devoted service of his brood, he swiftly switched to a stung and alert fellow with a sleeveful of tricks as he strove to keep a skip ahead.

In short, this is the story of that shocking period of a father's career—the era when he discovers that what Father says no longer goes. When he suggested that his newly married son and the son's wife move in with him and his younger son, Mr. Kraft, Senior, embarked on stormy waters. Successively he smashed against the reefs and shoals of the working wife, the businessman's weekend, vitamins, the skeletons in his closet, even saints. Social skies darkened, cultural gales howled, until, in a dramatic bind, the victim rashly disowned his elder son.

Yet who can say if Father lost the war? For he did last, until only the echoes of that hardest knock of all were left to chill him.

Ken Kraft

Big Sur, California

*Give Father a Hard Knock*

# 1.   *Father Has an Idea*

When my father was cruising through his mid-fifties, very recently widowed but otherwise in comfortable circumstances and of cast-iron habits, he entered the most traumatic phase of his domestic life. He did so almost casually and without fuss, like a sleepwalker sauntering into a brick wall. What is more, he proposed it himself, on an evening when he dropped by to call on my bride and me. We had been married less than a year and she was still experimenting with furniture arrangements and color schemes in the cottage we had leased in Webster Groves, a suburb of St. Louis.

"I was wondering," Father said, studying us through a cloak of smoke from his cigar, "what you'd think about moving in with Ted and me." Pat and I stared at him. He had given us no inkling of this plan. She said, "Oh?" and I said, "Well."

"Don't decide right now," said Father, who despised indecision. "Take awhile to talk it over." He shifted suddenly as if a spring in our secondhand easy chair had come loose and stabbed him, craning his neck at the uncluttered look of a newly established household as if taking inventory. "I've got that big place," he said presently, giving the impression he was at the moment visiting the children's playhouse. "Room for everybody." He cleared his throat. "Talk it over and let me know," he said, and left almost abruptly.

We talked it over for the rest of the evening. We were still talking after we had gone to bed and turned off the light. My father was not the easiest man to live with and I was just then cataloguing drawbacks, thinking out loud for my own benefit as well as my bride's. "Stubborn," I said. "Prejudiced and intolerant in many ways. Fairly vain. Quick-tempered——"

"Trustworthy?" she said suddenly.

"Well—sure," I said. "Yes, of course."

"Loyal?" she asked. I said he was extravagantly loyal. "Helpful?" she asked after a short pause.

I smiled in the dark. "Yes, helpful. And friendly, courteous, kind."

I could hear her laughing. "What comes next? Obedient?"

"Obedient, cheerful, thrifty, brave, clean, and reverent." It had not been so many years since I'd been a Boy Scout.

"Well?" she asked.

"Well," I said, "he certainly isn't thrifty."

We slept on it. By morning Pat, who had continued to hold her job after we were married, out of our necessity, told me at breakfast that she felt we ought to say yes. "For Ted's sake as much as for your father's," she said. My brother Ted was taking the pre-medical course at Washington University and had some hard years ahead. "I don't think he's getting the right kind of meals," she said. "When they were over here for dinner a couple of weeks ago I never saw a boy eat so much in my life."

"He's a bottomless pit," I said. "The thing is, how will it affect you and me to give up our own home at this point?"

"We're mature, I hope, and reasonably well adjusted. I'd hate to think we couldn't adapt to a simple new household situation."

Put this way, it seemed a challenge to our characters. "Well, I'm willing to give it a trial," I said. "We ought to know in six months if it's going to work and a whole lot sooner if it isn't." We decided to drive over and tell my father that evening, since we were both free and we thought it would relieve his mind to get the word from us in person right away.

His home was in University City, a suburb just west of St. Louis. The place was a two-story brick house in the mid-Coolidge style of architecture with a rash of interior glass doors and small colored-glass windows, and a sunroom hanging grimly onto one corner like a caboose.

We made our way up the red cement front walk and onto the red cement front porch. Father had evidently been going through a red phase when he built the house, for its red bricks were laid with reddish mortar and he had specified red shingles for the roof. Passers-by occasionally slowed down for a better look and sometimes removed their glasses and cleaned them hard. This pleased Father if he saw them. He was a natural style leader in such matters.

Pat, a step ahead of me, stopped short at the front door and peered through its filmy curtains. The door was mostly glass panes, and being flanked by similar tall windows, it made a sort of yoo-hoo-everybody entry. Through it we could easily see Father striding about the living room. He had in one hand a yardstick, a convenience he was never far from at home since he always had a dozen or so standing in handy corners. He was taking rapid measurements along one of the walls, and now and then he made a note on a scrap of paper.

He opened the door when we pressed the bell and seemed pleased to see us but without the anxious impatience he usually showed when awaiting some decision. I wondered if perhaps he had already repented an impulsive offer and now would just as soon we refused it. When neither of us mentioned it immediately he waved his yardstick in a room-embracing flourish. "Everything fits," he declared. We just

looked at him and he jabbed the yardstick in the air in mild
irritation. "Your furniture," he said. "It'll fit in here. There's
room. I measured." He was talking in the short and simple
sentences one uses with young children or backward adults,
I realized.

Pat began to laugh. "How did you know we'd decided,
Dad?"

"You have, haven't you?" he asked, and smiled placidly at
her nod. It struck me how typical this was of Father. He
expected things to turn out the way he preferred, from the
weather to his digestion and all points in between. This confidence seemed odd when you considered his attitude toward
certain common troubles of existence. These he called hard
knocks, and to hear him tell it, he had taken more hard
knocks than a Marine-band bass drum. I had no doubt he
had had his share, though he never gave me any details of
the knocks, perhaps because he considered me one of them.
At the moment none of us realized that in setting up this new
domestic chemical combination my father was letting himself in for brand-new hard knocks enough to last a more
cautious man twenty years. Thrift was not in him even here.

"I'm looking forward to this," he said to Pat. "You know,
I've always wanted a daughter." He aimed his yardstick at
the south end of the living room. "Now, your sofa could go
there. Mine can move to the other end, next to the piano."

Pat agreed. "And we've got those two big chairs. The
Cogswell . . ."

". . . can go in your bedroom," Father said. "Convenient
to have a nice big chair in a bedroom. Also that secretary
you're using for a china cabinet. And the other big chair'll
fit here along the west wall."

"All right," Pat said, measuring with her eyes. "Now—our
kneehole desk?"

Father and his yardstick moved a few feet farther down
the west wall. "We'll have to put it here at right angles, don't
you think?" My brother Ted, who had been upstairs study-

ing, came down, nibbling what seemed to be a dry prune, and greeted us.

"Our coffee table?" Pat asked Father. He placed it with his yardstick. "Console table?" Pat said. He indicated the spot, under a mirror facing the front door. "Tier table?" she said, taking a mental walk around our cottage living room. Father indicated a place at one end of one sofa.

Ted leaned toward me. "What do you do with all those tables?"

"There are only five small ones," I said, "and the dining room drop-leaf."

"Well, that's six," he murmured. "And there's already three in here. *Nine* tables in one room?"

"Ten if you count our kneehole desk. It's kind of a table." Ted hastily started gnawing another prune and offered me one from his pocket. "We have that plant stand, too," I said to him as Father continued to assign items to their stations. "And eight or so small chairs, the big footstool, that enormous mirror, brass bucket . . ." Ted and I blinked at each other as the list grew.

Pat and Father finished the placement. "The rest can go here and there," he said easily. "No problem." She agreed; their assurance was amazing. "Say . . ." He turned to me, seized by a sudden qualm. "You didn't sign a lease or anything?"

"A three-year one. The landlady——"

"*Three years!* You tied yourself up for three years?"

"Yes, but the landlady——"

"What's her name and address?" he said. "Better let me handle her."

"Thanks," I said, "but I spoke to her today. She understood the situation perfectly and she'll let us break the lease. She was very nice about it."

"That so?" Father said after a moment. "Well . . . all right, then." He looked slightly downcast, almost as if he wanted our landlady to set up a squawk for her rights so he could

charm her out of it. "Who's going to move you?" he asked
suddenly.

"Oh, anybody," Pat said. "We'll just look in the phone
book."

Father shook his head hard. He yanked a memo book from
his vest pocket and began jotting a reminder to himself in
his handsome, masculine handwriting. "Driemeyer's," he said
with authority. He surveyed us from the seat of management.
"Friends of mine and a good reliable old north-side firm. I'll
get in touch with them."

If you were a friend of Father's, you were a capable giant
in a world of ineffectual pygmies. Also, you paid your bills
on time, probably voted Republican, and rooted for the St.
Louis Cardinals baseball team.

## 2. *Father Starts the Day*

The three-week interval before Pat and I moved to my father's house would, I had thought, be plenty of time to give her a kind of basic training in his daily routine. Actually, in the turmoil of getting ready to move, all I had time to tell her about was the violent way he began his working day. I had always thought he would have made a splendid fireman from the manner in which he woke up when the alarm sounded. He achieved consciousness like a cat, all in one piece, and was ready to go the instant the small, shrill clock on a chair beside his bed rang. However, he turned it off and settled back for five minutes of strange indolence. It was the only five minutes of the day he deliberately wasted and he might just as well have not. In place of relaxing, he lay like a coiled spring, mentally speaking, waiting for the next signal. This came from a second alarm clock, in a bronze case setting on his bureau. It sounded like a metallic duck, and to turn off its quacking Father had to rise and travel across the room. Sometimes he had to turn it off two or three times, darting at it in between his setting-up exercises, as the turn-off mechanism was uncertain.

By this time anyone in the house not yet aroused and not drugged came to with a jump as he performed his calisthenics. He was not a huge man—six feet tall, 172 pounds on the bathroom scale—but he was solid and he did his morning workout the way he did everything, as if he had bet somebody he could break the speed record. His exercises were simple sorts. One was to bend and touch his toes, which caused his joints to make startling noises, like muffled gunfire. He also did an arm twirl, rapidly describing small circles with his outstretched hands, occasionally a bit too close to the low ceiling fixture. The most dramatic of the other exercises was the finale, in which he leaped into the air, clapping his hands over his head as he came down with feet spread, then leaped again and landed standing at attention. He did about ten of these, until he and the house were jumping in time, when he left off and strode to the bathroom across the hall. The exercises had taken him only three minutes, and he allotted the bathroom another ten, just about half the time he really took. As a result he was always trying to cut corners.

"Shaving takes too long," he often complained before electric razors came along, and he tried to eliminate waste motion, calculating that sixteen swipes with a safety razor should do the job. The main trouble was his chin. It jutted like a cowcatcher on an old prairie locomotive, and he could seldom mow it in the three scrapes it was allowed. Anyway, keeping count made him lose track of time, and when he installed an electric clock with a sweep-second hand in the bathroom he changed the system and raced the second hand, trying to shave while it made one round trip. He nicked hell out of his face, stealing peeks at the clock, and this bloodletting was stopped only by the arrival of electric razors. Father was entranced with them. "No more lathering, no more nicks," he declared, "and I'll save the time it takes for lotion." He made good speed on the maiden run and was satisfied the delightful gadget would soon have him consistently on the one-minute standard. It never got a chance to. He was fascinated with the tiny engine and found it far too interesting to hurry. Soon he was using something to make

the whiskers stand up better, stick talcum to dry his skin, and lotion again because it felt good. All in all, electric shaving took him two or three minutes longer than blade shaving, but he seemed to feel the higher standard of living was worth it.

He then tried to pick up the lost time by hurrying other things more. His large, square hands with relatively short fingers were not good at holding onto fragile things, and in his haste he dropped shaving-lotion bottles so often, the bathroom smelled like a barbershop a good deal of the time. His profanity was prosy but loud, and whenever something got away from him we would hear a roared "Dammit to hell," swiftly followed by the crash and a sound of dancing as he hopped to avoid flying glass.

Now and then his morning routine had to make room for
an effort to grow hair, whenever he found a new hope for it.
Except for a few die-hard strands he had no hair left on top.
When young he had had quite a crop, and he seemed to
feel it had departed by mistake and could be persuaded back.
At times he reminded me of a frantic cheerleader exhorting
a small and listless crowd to fight, dammit, fight. For a while
he had pinned his hopes on brushing his temple hair the
wrong way each morning, sending a perfect torrent of blood
up to encourage hair roots he presumed were alive but dor-
mant, like a bed of sulky onion sets awaiting warm weather.
However, the use of tonic to irrigate the follicles suited him
better, as it was faster and the tonics smelled like business.
Studying his head with a strong light and his magnifying
mirror, he could make out a fair and downy fuzz. But it
stayed fuzz, and he lost even that for a while when a mas-
sager he tried massaged the stuff clean off with an army of
tiny rubber fingers. This was the phase going on when Pat
and I moved in, and he was losing three or four minutes of
bathroom time hunting blankly for the lost fuzz. It kept him
running all through dressing and breakfast fixing. Literally
running, I mean. "What on earth is he doing?" my wife exclaimed, listening through the wall.

"Getting dressed," I said. "Evidently he's behind schedule."

"Does it make that much difference?" she asked. "With
the good position he holds?"

It did to Father. With him punctuality was so much a
virtue it was always in danger of becoming a vice. He was
assistant general sales manager at Mallinckrodt Chemical
Works and had been with the firm almost from the time he
left school. He was a perfect example of a company man,
even to keeping a photograph of the senior Mr. Mallinckrodt,
founder of the business, hanging on the living-room wall next
to his secretary-desk. In a working life that eventually ex-
ceeded forty years I suppose Father was occasionally late
getting to the job, but I'm not sure. "Why doesn't he get up
ten minutes earlier," Pat inquired, "and avoid all this fuss?"

I suppose he didn't because rushing was normal to him and the system worked.

Fully dressed in five minutes—and he was particular about his appearance—he shot out of his bedroom and thundered down the stairs to fix his breakfast. He had frequently fixed it himself even while my mother was living, because he could do it faster. He had water heating to soft-boil an egg while coffee percolated and bacon fried as he set the table and fetched in the morning paper. Unless he dropped the coffee-pot and broke something, all the operations dovetailed and at about ten minutes before seven o'clock he was finished eating and off to the garage, stuffing his pipe with cigar scraps as he went.

The effect a girl in the house would have on his rising setup apparently did not occur to Father until the last minute. The day before Pat and I were to move he dropped by our house and got me aside. "What time does she have to get to work?" he asked in an undertone.

"Office opens at eight o'clock," I said, and he clamped down hard on his pipe stem. It was the same time his own office began work.

"How long does it take her to get ready?" he then asked, and looked aghast when I said about half an hour, not counting breakfast.

"That's fairly fast, Dad," I said.

"Yes, I guess it is, at that," he said in a husky whisper, and I wondered why all the secrecy. He got an envelope from his coat pocket to make notes on and frowned at them awhile. "Dammit all," he said in an aggrieved tone when I finally asked if it was anything I could help with. "I can't take a shower *before* I take my exercise, can I?"

"No," I said, "but what of it?"

He gave me an exhausted look. I was never able to follow his mental shorthand. "I'm trying to work it *out*," he said. I continued to look at him. "Use your head," he said, raising his voice without realizing it. "There's only one bathroom.

This takes close timing. I've got to . . ." Pat, skipping past, around our displaced furniture, overheard and paused. Father looked as if he had been caught at the cookie jar. "I—um —I was trying to work out the way we'll have to use the bathroom," he muttered. "In the mornings." I suddenly realized he was wrestling with a sticky problem here, that in this new household he had proposed there would be certain invisible walls he must heed from now on. So must Pat and so must Ted. I alone could saunter casually through them all.

"I've been thinking about that, too," she said to Father, surprising me. "My office starts work at eight."

He nodded resignedly. "Yes. I'll just have to get up earlier." He looked glumly at his figures. "Now, if I'm out of your way by six-twenty——"

"Six-twenty!" Pat cried.

"I suppose I could make it six-fifteen," he said, almost groaning. Though I never heard him complain about having to get up early, he held desperately onto every last minute of legitimate bedtime.

Pat tapped his arm and he tore his eyes from his figures. "What time do you finish up in the bathroom now, Dad?" she asked.

It was the time for truth, not theory. "Six-thirty," he murmured.

"Then it's perfectly simple," she said. "You won't have to change a thing. I don't even get up till a quarter of seven." He was so overwhelmed at this abrupt solution to the dilemma that it didn't occur to him to wonder at his daughter-in-law's speed, and I sensed that he was in for enough shocks without needing to learn just then that she didn't get to the office at least fifteen minutes early the way he did but was pleased if she was no more than twenty minutes late.

# 3.  *Victims of the Vitamin*

"A simple new household situation"—so Pat had described our new setup. The formula for dynamite is also fairly simple, I am told, and we quickly discovered how explosive this household of four adults was apt to be. The thing that touched it off was food.

Father lost no time in getting down to brass tacks about dinner. He had been eating in restaurants a good deal in the previous few months and was hungering for home cooking again. Somewhat to his dismay, Pat had no plans to quit her job very soon and be a full-time homemaker, but she was, at least, going to cook dinner for us each evening. In this she would be helped by some advance preparations which Katy, a Negro woman who had been looking after the housework for Father, would do. This settled, Father was anxious to find out what time he could expect to sit down at the table. He was used to eating at six o'clock sharp.

"Well, if I get home here the time I got home in Webster Groves," Pat said, "we can eat at about seven o'clock."

"S-e-e-e-ven!" Father cried. Even by six he was always

half-starved, and anyway, he cherished familiar routine like a dog.

"If I could bring Pat home from work with me," I said, "it wouldn't take so long, of course." But I couldn't. My newspaper job's hours weren't dependable enough. Father took a deep breath and prepared to make a major sacrifice. "*I'll* bring her home," he said bravely. "I'll change my route." You had to know Father to know what this meant to him. He had been refining his route home from the office for twelve years, trying to avoid as much of the heavy traffic as he could. He had got it down so fine that he zipped through a succession of side streets and private short cuts stretching clear from north St. Louis to the west end as if he were riding on tracks. He kept up with all the daily variations throughout the route, such as new bumps and children playing shinny, like a Mississippi River pilot studying sand bars on the New Orleans run. Changing the journey would be akin to deserting an old friend. But food was a still older friend, and he was not a man to shrink from a hard decision. He switched to the new route at once, and on the first trip he and Pat made it home a little before six, breathing hard. In a week or so he managed to clip three or four minutes off this time by shooting through two handy alleys and across a small park, and Pat discovered she could sometimes keep her mind off the driving by concentrating fiercely on the dinner she was going to cook if the Lord spared her.

My young wife was not an expert at cookery, of course. However, she learned things quickly and she liked to cook. And, like many girls set loose in a kitchen, she loved to try out new ideas. I had got used to this by now, but Father didn't know what was coming, and his stomach had completely forgotten what things were like when he himself had been a bridegroom. A less positive type of man might have accepted a new situation without fuss, but Father was as positive as they came. The rest of us realized this, all right, but we overlooked a profound effect it was now having on him—and one that was going to give all of us lumps in the days ahead. The effect was a paterfamilias obsession. Father had abruptly become again in his own eyes a noble father-image, due the admiration, obedience, and devoted service of we three. Plainly he was harking back to his good old days when Ted and I were children at home and he was the boss. He thought it was going to be the same thing all over again, only better.

As a matter of fact, this was approximately the way things went for the first few days, and Father had every reason to congratulate himself on the new setup. To simplify things, Pat was sticking pretty closely to steaks or chops for dinner, and Father would have eaten steak or chops without complaint till his buttons popped. The only complaints were on my side, and they were not about the food. Although Father was obviously enjoying the meals, he didn't take the trouble to say so. This was normal for him, but I thought a beginner such as my wife needed to be cheered on a little. I tried to throw him a hint by spearing a bit of steak on my fork when Pat stepped out to the kitchen for a moment. I held my fork up at Father and silently licked my lips. Ted picked up the cue and assumed a pleased smile as he worked his eyebrows up and down. Father's chewing became slower and his eyes shifted uneasily from one of us to the other. He suddenly jabbed his own fork into a piece of steak, frowned at it for a moment, and then began chewing it hard. "I don't see much wrong with the meat," he said loudly as Pat came back.

I tried another tack presently. "Delicious asparagus," I said as I took another helping. Father gave no sign he heard.

"Delicious, delicious," Ted said, and handed the bowl to Father, who helped himself to eight more stalks and went right on eating.

We tried it again the next evening, Ted and I batting little bouquets across the table about the lamb chops and cauliflower and fruit cocktail. For all the effect it had on Father, we could have been talking Lapp. He finished his meal, made a remark or two about the likelihood of rain and the injustice of the tax on cigars, and went off for a clubby evening in the living room. I began to think I would have to throw subtlety aside, though I had never found Father easy to talk to. If in addition what I had to say was even remotely critical of him, he ruffled up and clacked his beak, so to speak. As it happened, I was saved the need of doing something. Pat saved me, unwittingly, by a drastic change in the menu. The meals she suddenly began to serve us were healthy enough, no doubt, but I couldn't blame anybody for not praising them.

The trouble was, my wife had suddenly discovered nutrition. She discovered it in a medical textbook on the subject that Ted had foolishly shown her, and she was swept up by the novelty. This, obviously, was the way to feed a family—check the chart of food values and plan balanced meals. Apparently we had been eating such unbalanced ones all our lives, it amazed her we weren't all lopsided. Ted did not realize what he had started until the night the liver came to the table. It was accompanied by brussels sprouts.

Father, who had mistaken the aroma coming from the kitchen for that of good honest steak, looked blankly at the liver on the platter. It looked like a piece of shoe leather, a trifle overtanned. He cleared his throat and spoke, firm and clear: "I don't care so very much for liver, Pat. Just so you'll know hereafter."

"I've never been very fond of it either," she said as he began sawing at it with the carving knife, "but you need more vitamin A, Dad."

Father, who had never had a vitamin aimed at him before, reared back. "What for?" he demanded after a moment.

"Eyesight, for one thing," Pat said promptly. "You work with papers all day under artificial light, so you burn up a lot of A." Father burned up a little more, staring harder at the leathery liver. He had always eaten purely by taste, and if his constitution had any objections, he didn't know it. Nor did he believe it. "Liver is also quite high in the B complex,

you know," Pat said. Father didn't know and didn't care. His
eyes shifted in a trapped way to the brussels sprouts. He
didn't exactly hate brussels sprouts, but he would probably
have tried stewed grass first if given the choice. He picked
up the bowl and started to pass it. "I don't care for——" he
said.

"They're to balance your meal, Dad," Pat put in at once.
"They're the vitamin C." Father paused, the bowl suspended.
"You need C for healthy tissues," she said earnestly. He
picked up the serving spoon and found the littlest sprout;
he put it on his plate with a martyred air and started to pass
the bowl again. "And you need C to build bones," Pat said.
Father spooned another sprout onto his plate and thrust the
bowl toward me. "Do you know that without vitamin C," Pat
said, her eyes wide, "you can get *scurvy?*" Father desperately
ladled out half a dozen more sprouts and passed the bowl
at last. I took a few to ward off scurvy and had some whole-
wheat bread, which she was serving, Pat said, because it was
high in phosphorus. When the meal was over, I had a little
talk with Ted.

"You and your nutrition course," I said. "I ate so much
phosphorus, I'll glow in the dark. Why'd you have to let her
read the book?" But the damage was done and my wife was
enthralled with this novelty. The next thing we knew, a
heavy-bodied molasses appeared on the table in place of
strawberry preserves and turnip greens in place of cauliflower. Father didn't even know what turnip greens tasted
like and had to ask what he was eating. It made him no
happier to find out. He didn't care much for the fresh fruit
Pat took to serving as dessert either. "I'd like some lemon
pie, Pat," he finally stated, after two days of raw apples.

She was perfectly agreeable and said she'd make the pie
the next day. She did, but the meal as a whole was one of
those that leave you a little hungry, and Father mentioned it.
He was now sounding a bit impatient, like a captain whose
pilot had forgotten the hang of steering the ship.

"But it's the calories, don't you see?" Pat cried. "Pie's so high in them."

Father stared at her. It was bad enough that the house was full of strange vitamins, but he had not expected calories too. "Not that any of us are *much* overweight," she added, "but as the meal planner, that's something I'll have to watch." I could see from Father's face that she had hit a very touchy spot. He knew quite well that he was the only one who was overweight—by six or seven pounds around the middle, where it showed—but he had no intention of doing anything about it. He abhorred the idea of dieting. He withdrew from the table, his attitude thoughtful.

"I wonder if he still wishes one of us had been a daughter," Ted muttered to me afterward.

"Listen," I said, "maybe if you left that crazy nutrition text in your locker at school——"

"I left it there days ago," he said. "She must've memorized the charts." He looked at me crossly. "Nutritionwise, she's 100 per cent, but appetitewise, zero. She's your wife—why don't you put your foot down?"

"I hate to discourage her," I said. "And this is probably just a phase."

"Phases," Ted said darkly, "have been known to last for years."

Father may have heard of this too. It would account for the speed with which he acted, now that the question of weight control had entered the health picture. And if what he did was not exactly what you'd expect from a man who had just started out to be the czar of his new household, it did give a sudden glimpse of his foxiness.

"Oh, by the way, Pat," he said as we sat down the next night to creamed chipped beef (we needed the milk for calcium, she had mentioned), "I brought home a little present for you. I'll get it for you when dinner's over." He dived into the chipped beef, an entree he regarded as only a short step ahead of sowbelly, with good humor. When he had finished dinner with a slice of pineapple as though he enjoyed it, he appeared to have forgotten the present and Pat had to remind him.

"Oh, it isn't much," he said, going to the hall closet for it. "But seeing that you're interested in cooking and all . . ."

He handed her a gift-wrapped parcel about the size of the St. Louis telephone directory. "It feels like a book," she said, ripping off the wrapping. "Why, it's a cookbook," she exclaimed, staring at the exposed jacket. "A magnificent cookbook," she cried, leafing through it rapidly. "Just look at these photographs—in full color!"

"Pictures, eh?" Father said, unfolding an evening newspaper. "Well, I just happened to notice it on a counter when I was downtown today."

"It's *full* of pictures," she said. "Look."

He glanced at one. "'Roast duck with orange sauce,'" he said, reading the legend. He returned his eyes to the newspaper. "Probably too complicated."

"It doesn't sound so complicated," Pat said, reading the recipe. She read a few more. "None of them do." She leafed along, reading off some of the names as she went: "Gnocchi . . . rissole . . . eggs Meyerbeer . . . rum baba . . . cherries jubilee . . . peach *flambé* . . . tenderloin of beef *en brochette* . . . veal scallopini . . . roast stuffed suckling pig . . . sukiyaki . . . crown roast of lamb. . . ."

Father appeared to be listening with only half an ear, but now and then he swallowed hard. My own mouth was watering, too, and I could hear Ted's stomach growling clear across the living room.

"Crown roast of lamb," Father said, lowering his newspaper. "Now what do you suppose that looks like?"

"Here it is, right here," Pat said. She showed him the colored photograph, printed on heavy glossy paper. "'Two racks of lamb chops formed into a ring, with mushroom stuffing, garnished with sweet pickled peaches.'"

Father's eyes glazed momentarily. "All those pretty little

paper frills on top, too," he murmured. "Thing like that must be a terrible lot of trouble to cook."

"It sounds quite simple, really," Pat said, studying the recipe. "These directions are very easy to follow. For instance, here's a recipe that makes popovers clear to me for the first time. And here's one for a fluffy chocolate cream pie that would be fun to do; you top it with whipped cream pressed through a cake decorator."

Father made a supreme effort to pay attention to the sports section of the St. Louis *Post-Dispatch*. "It sounds," he said, swallowing vastly, "sort of interesting," and he disappeared behind the paper.

Pat put in the rest of the evening plowing back and forth through her new cookbook, marking with bits of paper certain pages with especially exciting recipes, and making out a shopping list. By the time bedtime came I was wide-awake, thinking hard about food and Father. Maybe he hadn't forgotten as much about a bride's cooking quirks as I had thought. Or—maybe he had reasoned that the way to deal with a woman's phase was with a new phase? Life in this household might have certain important results for me, I grasped. Suddenly this father was not the same father I had known all my life. Under an unfamiliar stress he had just become a man of guile and flummery, willing to stoop to tricks merely to win. He might well be worth a young man's closest study.

# 4. *Revolution in the Living Room*

His dazzling success at the dinner table may have been what encouraged Father to take his next step in molding the household nearer to his heart's desire. Or it may merely have been triggered when he almost broke his neck falling over our footstool. At any rate, he now began muttering, "Footstool, coffee table, big brass bucket. . . . Too many *things* in here." Every item he mentioned was something Pat and I had brought along.

"But it was his own idea to set things up in this way," I said to her. "Now he'll just have to live with it."

"So will we," she said, "and the living room *is* pretty crowded."

The trouble was, Father had overestimated the room. It was a weakness he had about his whole house and everything in it. He had once made a tour through one of the fine old St. Louis mansions that had been made a historic landmark, and he had set a kind of record for visitors' comments, I suppose. He made only one, toward the end of the tour. Nodding at a superb stained-glass window in the reception hall, he

said in a ringing voice, "Same as mine but not as neat." He
referred to a pair of small windows of red and green glass at
the north end of his living room. Each time Christmas came
around they looked nice.

The footstool over which Father had fallen presently found
its way, at his suggestion, up to the bedroom Pat and I occu-
pied. It was not a great inconvenience there, and its passing
seemed to make the living room much roomier. But only for
a day or two, so it was soon followed by a drop-leaf table,
our brass bucket, coffee table, and fern stand, and two small
chairs. These things arrived one at a time and the total effect
crept up on me. Most of them Father carried upstairs himself, after a word with Pat, if I was not there to carry them.
But when the chairs appeared and took up the only bit of
space left on any bedroom wall, I felt it was high time to file
a protest.

"Our bedroom's looking more like a living room than the
living room is," I said to Pat, "and I'm getting tired of barking
my shins in the dark here."

"Well, we won't need to shift things around any more,"
she said. "This is about all there is to move up here."

"After all," I said, "he asked us to come here, didn't he?
Now he acts as if the setup's giving him claustrophobia."

"If you must know, I don't mind this," she said. "Because
his things look terrible with most of ours." This had not occurred to me, but certainly Father liked things new and
modern, while our stuff was in the period styles—Chip-
pendale, Duncan Phyfe, Sheraton. Everything Father had
bought in recent years was angular or overstuffed or all glass
and chromium. Why not have a little style, he always said,
as long as you were spending the money.

Pat, however, had underestimated the effect a 100-proof
dose of Father's furniture would have on her. Though he
felt the living room had become homey again, the place began to give her indigestion merely to spend an entire evening
there. I had got pretty used to Father's taste over the years

but I felt sympathetic twinges for my wife. The upholstered things among his items were covered in a kind of seasick-purple mohair, and Pat finally settled on these as the most poisonous. "I don't mean to be temperamental or anything," she told me, "but living with your father's furniture is giving me a funny feeling. Like being smothered, sort of. Do you know what I mean?"

"Yes, in a general way," I said. "I had the same sensation once when he gave me a necktie he was through with. A red and blue Persian pattern. It nearly throttled me."

"Everyone has a perfect right to his own personality," she said, "but your father seems to have so much of it." I said he probably didn't realize he was more or less asphyxiating people with it, and she said she supposed not but we'd have to assert ourselves or get to be just rubber stamps.

"Got any ideas?" I said.

"Well, yes," she said. "I thought I'd make some slip covers."

Her idea seemed to be that the slip covers would hide the worst of the furniture and would symbolize a blow for liberty. What she told Father was just as true but less controversial. "With Ken and me here," she said, "your furniture is getting more wear, Dad. We ought to protect the overstuffed pieces."

He looked at her approvingly. "The finest mohair money can buy."

"And they certainly deserve slip covers," she said promptly. But the term stirred dark memories in Father. He frowned. "Those sheet things people used to drape all over furniture in summer? Well, I don't think——"

"Heavens, not those old-fashioned things," Pat said, and I saw she was learning fast. Father was in a continual revolt against old-fashioned things of his youth. "Today's slip covers are like pretty upholstery," Pat said.

"That's different," Father said. "I like things stylish."

She smiled. "Then I'll look at material next time I'm downtown. Maybe hand-blocked linen in a good flower design."

"Charge it to me," Father said grandly. "At Famous-Barr." He didn't have to specify; Pat had already found how slavishly devoted he was to Famous, one of St. Louis' three big department stores. Though he maintained charge accounts at the others—Stix-Baer-Fuller, and Scruggs, Vandervoort & Barney—the accounts almost died of malnutrition each year. Father simply could not resist a bargain, and in addition to competitive pricing Famous gave Eagle stamps. For a hundred dollars' worth of purchases you got stamps enough to fill a book worth $2.50 in trade at the store or $2 in cash. Father always took it out in trade, usually after accumulating such an astonishing credit balance in stamps that department buyers must have suspected he was front man for a pool-purchase club. It was merely that he loved to spend money, so naturally he piled up a lot of stamps. "I only buy what I need," he said, and he needed almost everything he saw.

Pat lost no time in shopping for material, as if she feared Father might change his mind. And he might have if he had been along on the buying expedition. My wife, it turned out, had never made a slip cover in her life. "It isn't very hard, is it?" I heard her asking the clerk. "Nothing to it, dearie," said the clerk, obviously a domestic-science major. "Just you lay the material on the furniture wrong side out, cut it to fit, pin the seams, take it off, and sew 'em up."

"I didn't know you were flying blind," I said to her. "Are you sure you can do this?"

"Oh-h-h, it all sounds simple enough," she murmured. "You heard her, didn't you?"

There was an old sewing machine in the house, one my mother had bought thirty years before. Pat had already found she could thread it and make it go, after a fashion. It was a Singer chain-stitch machine, about half the usual size and intended mainly for fine millinery work, according to some yellowed instructions my wife discovered in one of its drawers. "Mother couldn't have sewed a hat to save her soul," I said. "She must have bought this in a burst of girlish enthusiasm."

"It'll work fine," she said, "and now to cut the material and pin the pieces together. That'll take about an evening." She was wildly optimistic about her speed. Maybe she was tired when she got home from her job and had to fix dinner and all, but the cutting and pinning turned out to be a fearful job. After one evening she recruited me, and after the second evening we brought Ted in on it too. Only Father remained a spectator as we three snipped and pinned, muttering and pricking our fingers. "This is very nice," he said, watching approvingly while we bickered hotly over a wing-chair curve. "All the family working happily at home together." We wondered if his mind was suddenly slipping. Actually, though, in one respect Father was very old-fashioned, almost prehistoric; he wanted his tribe around him at the fireside.

For a beginner, my wife had set herself quite a task—four chairs and two sofas to slip cover. And when she tackled the sewing at last, she nearly gave the whole thing up. "It's such a little bitty sewing machine," she cried as she tried to ram thirteen yards of linen through the saucer-sized space between needle assembly and the drive-belt side. "And on some of the corners," she added, "it has to sew through four or five thicknesses of linen. I'm scared to death I'll break the needle."

"Don't worry about that," said Ted, who was watching her progress at the machine with an almost professional interest. "I've sewed canvas on it."

Pat turned to stare at him. *"Canvas!"*

"I made a knapsack once when I was a Boy Scout. Sewed through seven thicknesses in places." Pat had her mouth open to say something, but the seven thicknesses left her speechless. "It'll sew leather, too," Ted added, "if you turn the wheel by hand." Although she seemed to shudder, there must have been something reassuring about his remarks. She plunged ahead on the slip covers with such new verve that it caught Father's eye.

"Nothing like having good tools to work with," he said, nodding at the little machine as Pat pumped the wee treadle and stuffed yardage through the doll-sized slot. "A person could make a living with a nice machine like this one."

It took two weeks of evenings and weekends to accomplish the slip covers and it wore out everybody but Father. If anything, he became fresher. Though he seemed to pay only occasional attention to the details of the job, he tossed out suggstions from time to time to speed things up or improve them. Some of the suggestions were surprisingly good when you considered that the tool he was handiest with was a hatchet. With a hatchet he could have built a house. His advice on the slip covers gave him more of a proprietary interest in them, and when at last they were finished and on the furniture he was as pleased as if he had invented them. "Now we need a new rug," he said suddenly.

Pat tried to hide her joy. The old rug gave her chills, having a sort of cabbage pattern in mauves and greens. "A nice gray one would look good," she said. Father cocked his head. "Or beige," she said. "A good rule is to pick something from among the colors in the slip cover."

"Ah," Father said, looking brightly at the flowery slip covers.

Pat was still not used to the speed with which Father could act when he was going to buy something. She had expected to take a few weeks looking at all the rugs in town. The very next evening Father announced at dinner: "I bought the rug today."

"You b-b-b-*bought* it?" Pat cried. "Already?"

"And I got a good buy, too," he said.

"Is it gray?" she asked numbly.

Father chuckled as if she had made a joke. "It's a surprise," he said. "Be delivered tomorrow."

It arrived the next day, and after dinner Ted and I took

up the old rug at Father's direction and unfurled the new. It had reds and blues and golds and greens and pinks and purples and God knows what all, a roaring fruit salad of a rug. As it rolled forth, Pat tried to stifle a gasp, not successfully. Father took it for pure delight. "I knew you'd like it," he said. "Talk about colors!"

"It's . . . certainly got those," she murmured, casting a despairing glance at the overpowered slip covers. They weren't in the same league with the rug. They looked like last week's bouquet. Ted and I finished the unrolling and walked back across the rug. It was like strolling through a field of powder puffs. It felt so expensive I wanted to take off my shoes.

"It's an oriental, you know," Father said. "All the best places have them. And with all the colors in those slip covers, I knew we had to have something good and bright."

Pat appeared too bushed to say much, and Ted and I found ourselves blinking from close exposure to the pattern. The room seemed to shimmer now, a total change from what it was before rug and before slip covers. Yet somehow it seemed once again to have become an extension of Father's personality. "I bought it at Famous," he said contentedly. "They give Eagle stamps."

# 5. *The Compleat Churchman*

His triumph in the living room undoubtedly had something to do with Father's next step toward a calculated dictatorship. It was evident to me that he had given the matter profound thought. He was so casual about it. "I was thinking I might take everybody out to noon dinner tomorrow," he said on Saturday evening.

"Fine, I can save the roast till Monday," Pat said.

"Nice to eat out once in a while," Father added. He was usually as fond of it as of hemlock. "And," he said to her, "you've been working so hard on the slip covers." Hearing no static, he swooped: "We can go directly from church. That way we'll beat the Sunday rush."

Ted and I exchanged hooded glances. This was an old story to us, Father's little plots to get us to church. We were not heathens but we felt no urgency to follow his example in weekly attendance. He was as regular as the rector himself, Mr. Lightfoot. It was Mr. Lightfoot, in fact, who had turned Father from the primrose path. Until then he had no more interest in church than he had in raffia work. My mother had attended services now and then, and Ted and I had gone to the Sunday School, but Father felt no need of spiritual refreshment until one evening when Mr. Lightfoot paid him a call at home. Instead of hammering him over the head with the Bible as some previous rectors had done, Mr. Lightfoot laid it on the line in a way Father understood at once. "It takes money to run a church," the rector said, "and I need help in lining up the annual pledges." He referred to commitments for contributions. "I need some businessmen to work with me," he said bluntly.

Father was entranced with this practical approach. Although he had always assumed he would see us all in heaven later on, he seemed to feel the details could wait. Once Mr. Lightfoot had got to him, however, he became an active force in the church militant and a swift scourge to all financial backsliders in the parish. This activity had continued ever since, and when Pat and I joined his household he was a long-time pillar of the church—a member of the vestry and its senior warden, confidant of the rector on worldly matters, and head usher in charge of the Sunday collection.

"You mean you want all of us to go to church with you tomorrow, Dad?" Pat asked.

"It would work out better that way," he murmured. "Timing and all."

"All right," she said after a mere moment's thought. "I guess it would." Ted and I felt we had been betrayed. We knew our father well. Give him a crumb and he would seize a loaf. Did Pat, we wondered, quite realize? . . .

A drawback about going to church or anywhere else with Father was that you were on your mark to get ready to get set to go from the moment you agreed. "The service starts at eleven," he said, snatching paper and pencil from his pocket. "We'll leave here at ten-fifteen. Means we'll have to be all finished with breakfast by quarter of nine. Have to start eating by eight. Half hour to fix—begin by seven-thirty. Get up by seven. Or better make it six-thirty——"

"Six-thirty on a *Sunday* morning?" Ted chirped. "Count me out."

Father bristled at him. Ted had not inherited his passion for punctuality. "This is a family thing," he barked. "I've been telling——" He checked himself but the cat was out of the bag. It was instantly plain to all three of us that he had been telling someone—almost surely Mr. Lightfoot—that he was going to show up at church with his whole kit and kaboodle trailing him down the aisle like docile chicks behind the prideful rooster. This alone would have been enough to make Ted and me decline absolutely; Father was worse than a lawyer for springing on precedents. But Pat, alack, was not so informed as we. She shattered what should have been a united front and said airily to Ted, "It won't kill you to get up a little early tomorrow morning. Anyway, if you're going to be a doctor you'll have to get used to things like that." Father looked at her with admiration; he was always charmed to get a new argument he could bang Ted with and he could see there was a lot of mileage in this one.

He and Pat arranged the logistics of breakfast, and he polished his shoes before he went to bed, to give him a head start. "Well, you've done it now," I said to Pat. "Put a whip in his hand. Whether or not we ever go to church with him again, he'll nag us every Sunday. Aren't we having problems enough in this house?"

She widened innocent eyes. "Why, I think it'll work out fine. After all, he takes such an interest in religion."

"In church," I said. "Not in religion. He hasn't heard a sermon in years." She looked skeptical. "That's when he counts the collection," I said. "In the choir room during the sermon. Of course he claims he listens, if you ask him, but he never did, even before he took on counting the money."

"Oh, you're exaggerating," she said, getting ready to go to bed. "He can't help but hear it." Father's ears were excellent, but he had a talent for turning them off.

Organized up to the eyebrows, we left for church approximately on schedule the following morning and got there

early enough to have a wide choice of pews. Father flour-
ished us to a front center one, seated us, and backed off. "I
have to look after things," he whispered, sounding executive.
"I'll join you here right after the service."

I nudged Ted. "All right," I hissed to Father. "We'll tell
you what the sermon was all about."

He paused in flight. "I listen to the sermon," he said distinctly. "I hear every word in the choir room. Every syllable."

He marched off and Pat smirked at Ted and me. We
folded our arms and held our peace.

Mr. Lightfoot was a rector who took his sermon seriously.
He was a large man, of imposing figure in the pulpit in his
robes, and he had earnestness and eloquence. He was not a
hell-fire–damnation preacher at all. Skirting the dreadful and
dramatic, he made thoughtful excursions each Sunday into
faith and ethics, compassion and responsibility. He was, all
in all, a very high-class type of preacher, as Father had often
said. His topic this Sunday was "The Duty of Ability."

As he got into it, with examples both Biblical and literary,
I became aware of a rustling next to me, and on looking, I
found my wife making a few notes on a bit of paper, in
shorthand. While I had always listened to Mr. Lightfoot
with interest, it had never occurred to me to immortalize
him in notes. Father, I thought, would be dazzled by this
show of interest when he heard. And in a sense I suppose he
was.

He joined us promptly after the service ended, as the exo-
dus was getting under way. By then Mr. Lightfoot had quit
the altar for his study just off the transept and, gathering up
his robes, had raced around outside the church, to shake
hands with the first parishioners to leave. It was a weekly
feat he performed, and it demonstrated his good physical
shape that he was never observed panting when he hit the
front door.

Father paraded us out to the vestibule, bowing and in-
troducing en route, to salute the rector and depart. As we

did so, my wife tarried to say something nice to Mr. Lightfoot about a point he had made in his sermon. He seemed
pleasantly amazed but no more so than Father. "By George,
I bet he doesn't know what hit him," Father exclaimed when
we were outside. "He doesn't get much of that out of *this*
congregation."

"Much of what?" Pat inquired, as if she had been somewhere else.

"Sensible talk," Father said. He did not mean that the
other parishioners were fools, but he was not very good at
elaborating. Nor did he usually have to with Pat; they could
carry on a conversation in a kind of code, I had found, with
half-finished sentences, solitary words, even gestures and
noises, while Ted and I looked on, utterly in the dark. Today,
however, Pat seemed as dense as we.

"All I did was tell him I thought his point about the historical perspective of the story of the talents was illuminat-
ing," she said.

"That's what I mean," said Father as we got into the car
and he aimed it for the restaurant he had in mind.

"Well, I can't take much credit for that," she said. "It was
so obvious." Father did not answer. "At least," Pat added, "I
thought Mr. Lightfoot made it very plain." Father looked
hard out of the windshield.

"He's all right," Ted said. "He doesn't preach your ears
off."

"That's it," Father said heartily. "That's what I like about
him. He says it and gets it over with. You can almost set
your watch by him." He pulled up in front of the restaurant,
and for a few minutes we were too busy keeping him in sight
to talk. As he had estimated, we were a few minutes ahead
of the peak-hour crowd, and he didn't intend to lose his advantage. We all streaked to the table he picked and sat down,
breathing a little hard, while he summoned a waiter and
rapidly ordered the meal with a minimum of consultation.
His manner in a restaurant invariably inspired waiters with
the idea he was about to miss a train. This suited Father

just fine, and today it turned out to have a special advantage.

"I think your church is fortunate to have a man with Mr. Lightfoot's imaginative scope, Dad," Pat said, when the waiter had galloped off with our order.

Father blinked. "Well, I suppose so," he said.

"Oh, I'm sure of it," she said. "Such as in the striking comparison he made between Lincoln and Edison. You know?"

As she waited, Father took a quick swig of water and then a couple more. "Lincoln," he said at last, clearing his throat. "Abraham Lincoln?"

"In his point about the basic relevance of abilities," Pat said. "Don't you remem——"

Father jerked his head around. "Here comes the shrimp cocktail," he cried, spying the waiter speeding toward us. He welcomed the man like a lost brother and urged him to keep up the good work. While we were eating the shrimps the waiter picked up a minute or two by bringing the salads on ahead of the entrees, and Father started on his salad the moment he had finished his shrimps. This so hampered conversation that the rest of us went ahead on our salads too. But being a fast eater, Father finished his salad before the main course had time to get there. He was reaching for the bread when Pat glanced up. She had been looking in her purse as if for a compact or handkerchief, but she produced neither.

"Then there's this question of an ethical quarantine that Mr. Lightfoot raised," she said briskly. "I think I see why he related it to natural ability, but I'd like a man's reaction to——"

"Here comes the fried chicken," Father shouted, and indeed it was, at a trot. "Don't let it get cold," he said rapidly when the waiter had set the plates around, and he immediately set an example by beginning. He did not ordinarily talk much during a meal, and this one was no exception. His only remarks, made at approximately the same times Pat seemed about to say something, dealt with the food, and he did not encourage anyone to linger on when we had finished.

To my surprise and pleasure, he did not then suggest taking a drive. I had expected it and was thinking up some good
excuses. Sunday afternoons were when Father went for joy
rides, a term that had no truth for his passengers. His object
was to cover as much ground as possible, roughly the same
ground he had covered the previous Sundays, in the west
and north parts of St. Louis County. The south end of the
county he had nothing to do with. He felt like a foreigner
there.

He headed directly for home as soon as he had observed
the outlines of good manners by saying he supposed everyone wanted to go there and then starting off with a rush.
The Sunday traffic on Delmar Boulevard, while brisk, was
not nearly so heavy as that which he had to suffer through
on weekdays, but if it had been, I don't think he would have
minded just then. As it was, he had time to talk. Or to be
talked to.

"As I was saying," Pat said, "Mr. Lightfoot certainly gives
you something to take away. He really gets to the heart of
things. Or don't you agree, Dad?"

"Very good minister," Father said hurriedly. "Everybody
speaks well of him. My, isn't this traffic a change from weekdays?"

"Quite a change," Pat said. "And speaking of that, Mr.
Lightfoot is quite a change from a lot of ministers."

"Uh—yes," Father mumbled, working his head up and
down.

"I'm so glad we went with you, Dad," she said. "It just
goes to show—you never know what'll come of going along
with a suggestion."

"No," Father said heavily, "you don't."

"There were some other things, too . . ." Pat said, and
broke off to rummage in her purse for her slip of paper. "Oh
yes. The sin of ignoring one's destiny. That was very thought-
provoking, I felt. And this other, identifying oneself with
ultimate——"

"Is that *shorthand?*" Father exclaimed, twisting his neck to look queerly at her slip of paper.

"A few notes I made during the sermon," she said. "So I wouldn't look stupid when we talked about it. After all, *you're* used to hearing Mr. Lightfoot's sermons." Father did not reply. He stepped harder on the gas and began passing everything in sight. "When you're not used to a minister," Pat said, "it's harder to remember. Now you probably never have any trouble . . ." She squeaked as Father skinned around a poky sedan and shot down our street. He came to a blazing stop in front of the house, and three of us got out. Pat paused on the sidewalk, holding her shorthand notes, and looked back. "Aren't you coming in, Dad?" she asked. The car was already rolling.

"I've got some things to do," he muttered. "And don't wait supper on me. I'm not sure what time I'll be back."

When the next weekend rolled around, Ted and I crossed our fingers and waited. Pat, apparently absorbed in worldly things, had made no more mention of Mr. Lightfoot's silver

tongue, and Father could have been a pantheist for all you could have told from his strict silence on religious topics.

He said nothing at the dinner table Saturday night about going to church en masse. Then he went to the living room and read through the evening papers. He said nothing at all until finally he was ready to go upstairs to bed. Then he said it, and it seemed to take quite a bit out of him. "About church tomorrow," he murmured, seeming to address Pat in a general sort of way. "If you're going, we'd better see about getting up on time and all."

"Oh, I don't think I can make it tomorrow, Dad," she said. "I have some things to do."

"Me, too," I said, and Ted said he had to study.

Father stood blinking at us for a few moments as if he could hardly credit his ears, but he accepted our desertion with admirable poise. An observer not in the know might have made the mistake of thinking someone had just given him a present, from the look on his face. "Well, good night, then," he said, and skipped up the stairs humming a brave snatch of song.

"I guess I'm getting used to this new oriental rug of Dad's," Pat said out of the blue a little while later. "I don't seem to mind it quite as much."

"It has its points," I said. "It makes other rugs look bankrupt."

"I find," Ted said, "that it's a very nice rug to walk barefoot on."

# 6.  *All Work and a Yard Wide*

By now I was entirely convinced my father was a man of
many talents and had better be kept under scrutiny. For one
bent on recognition as the coddled star of his new family,
this was a dubious status, akin to that of the man reported
as hollering to be honor guest. But either Father did not realize this or he accepted it as a pesky but temporary situation.
Also, he could lose a battle without despairing of the war; he
dropped the en masse church attendance like a scorpion and
snatched up the next item on his secret agenda. The spring
weather had turned nice, and like a weathercock he turned
with it. It was the season for him to become a country gentleman—and now what a country gentleman he could become, thought he, with three stout aides to fetch and carry,
if he could arrange it.

At heart Father was the squire type, and if he had been
born to land and money there would have been no living
with him. As it was, with nothing more than a suburban lot
to dabble on, he was known by name to the St. Louis Seed
Company and three nurseries, and his annual descent on

his yard was the signal for the rest of the neighborhood to
wake up and fly for their hoe handles. They were not terribly competitive, but watching Father made them nervous.

It would have made anyone nervous, and a landscape ar-
chitect would have been a wreck. "Nature," Father once
stated, "is nice," and he believed in helping her along. When
he made a flower bed he gave it an extra flourish in some
way, such as by building a rock retaining border on the lines
of a heavy-duty dam. Trellises sprouted here and there, with
or without vines, and there was a forty-pound stone sundial
that had to be moved each time the grass was cut, along with
a pottery birdbath. A sponge rock structure that looked like
a small well and was a sham jutted hard by a peach tree,
and if you crossed the grass to the far middle of the yard
you suddenly found yourself treading a little brick walk; it
ran around a bed of roses and then stopped as abruptly as it
had started. Everything in the yard was a copy of some fea-
ture Father had admired somewhere else—at a garden show,
a park, some public building—though "copy" is not the right
word. His method was to digest what he admired and then
produce his own version of it consistent with space, time, and
money. Thus, having once thrilled to the sight of a reflecting
pool five hundred feet long and fifty wide, he had come home
bearing a silvered gazing globe for the back yard.

By the time Pat and I moved into the house, Father had
been some years at the construction phases of the yard. His
more recent improvements included a combined goldfish
pool and rock garden on the back line; another goldfish pool
in the side yard—superior to the other because it had a drain
and did not need to be cleaned by dipping and sponging,
when the drain worked; concrete curbings for the driveway,
incorporating a tigerish tire-killer curve; several short rock
walls here and there; a set of Adirondack lawn chairs; and a
birdhouse, untenanted. Plainly there was not much farther
he could go in this direction, and it turned out he had no
intention of doing so. This year was to be a year of realiza-

tion, a year of the flowering, fruiting earth. We learned of it at dinner the next Friday night.

"I brought home a few rosebushes," Father said. The three of us looked politely, impersonally interested. "This year," he added, "I'm going to do it right."

Pat fell for the bait. "Do what right, Dad?"

"Colors," he cried triumphantly. "I'm going to do the colors right. No more mixed-up beds." I suppose we all looked blank at this, because he hurriedly finished his dessert and said, "Come on—I'll show you." We followed him to the back yard, where he took up a commanding position near the fake well. "All yellow," he said, aiming a forefinger at a rock-ribbed bed along the north line. "All white," he said, moving to the next bed. "All red," pointing to the brick-walk bed, "and all pink," at a bed along the driveway. He turned to us. "Now, won't that be beautiful?"

There seemed no reason to argue. It was his yard, wasn't it? He could have planted Jimson weed for all we cared. We told him it would be gorgeous, and then Pat happened to ask a question of peculiar significance. "But are you sure you remember what color rosebushes you already have here, Dad?"

He made airy motions with his hands. "They're played out anyway. We'll just pull them up and throw them away."

"Did you happen to notice," I said to Pat afterward, "that he said *we'll* pull them up?"

"So he did," she murmured. "I wonder if he's planning——"

"I have to study," Ted said. "I'm going to be a doctor."

"After all, it's his hobby, not ours," I said. "We still have to go downtown tomorrow morning, and we might go to a show after lunch." Pat bit her lip and frowned at the back yard, where Father was still hobbying.

Weekends, to Father, did not mean lying abed. He permitted himself the luxury of waking up in the morning naturally, but he naturally woke up at 6 A.M. anyway. He would then have been willing to allow himself as much as fifteen

minutes of dawdling in bed before rising, but the instant he
awakened, his mind began planning the day, and after five
minutes he was so full of notions that he couldn't stand it any
longer. In consequence he was always long through with his
breakfast by the time the rest of us rose. This morning as we
traipsed down to the kitchen, yawning and stretching, he
was buzzing about the back yard, lining up tools, stacking
new bare-root rosebushes in the shade, pending planting,
and pulling out the hose. As we sat down at the table, he
came hurrying in and rushed upstairs. Three or four minutes
later he came down wearing a collar and tie and dressed in a
suit. "I have to get some fertilizer," he said, striding outside
after a swift glance at our breakfast progress. "Be right back."

"Well, for heaven's sake," Pat said after a few moments.
"He got all dressed up just to go to the store?"

"Listen," I said, "I've seen him polish his work shoes before
he started to mow the front lawn."

She shook her head in mystification, and before we were
finished eating, Father was back with three sacks of fertilizer
in his car trunk. He raced upstairs again to change back to
his work outfit—an old pair of trousers and a shirt that looked
neater than the things I wore every day.

"I think you boys had better give him a hand unloading
those sacks," Pat said. "They're heavy."

We hurried out and hoisted the hundred-pound sacks from
the trunk while Father was still leaping into his work clothes
and were dusting off our hands when he arrived. "Not here!"
he cried, seeing where on the lawn we had dumped the sacks.
We put them where he pointed, five feet northeast. When
Father planned a job he planned it right down to the last
detail, and sometimes the one helping him had to wait till
it was all finished to find out what they'd been doing. Ted
and I left at a trot while he was busy opening one of the
fertilizer sacks. "Three hundred pounds of it," I said to Pat
when we returned to the house. "You'd think he was feeding
Shaw's Garden."

She gazed moodily out of the window, tapping her lower

lip with one finger. "Well, if we're going downtown . . ." she said, and we finished breakfast and went upstairs to dress. From the window there we had an excellent bird's-eye view of Father. He had begun yanking out the doomed rosebushes. Now and then he threw a restive glance toward the house.

"How about dropping me off at the campus?" Ted asked when we were ready to leave. "I think I can keep my mind on my work better there."

"All ready?" I said, my hand on the knob of the back door. Ted got a firm grip on his books. Pat nodded. Outside we could see Father already spading the new yellow-rose bed, now bare of old bushes. He was perspiring a little about the forehead, and he paused to remove his hat, a straw sailor with a striped ribbon, and wipe the inside band with his handkerchief. As he did so he stared hard at the back door and we emerged, descended the porch steps, and crossed the yard, shoulder to shoulder. Father's jaw dropped.

"You're moving right along with it, I see," I remarked, nodding agreeably at him.

Ted regarded the mess fleetingly. "Looks swell," he said in a hurry.

"Ken and I are going downtown, Dad," Pat said, and twisted her handkerchief. "We'll be back in time for me to fix dinner tonight, of course." Father, looking splotchy in the face and breathing hard, said nothing. We all climbed into my coupé and I backed it out of the driveway. "Not too fast today," Pat murmured. Father never backed his car out of the driveway, preferring to jockey it around by a dozen gees and haws in the wide space in front of the garage, and I sometimes backed out extra fast just to stand his hair on end. Today I left more sedately, but Father was not watching. The muscles of his jaws bulging, he had resumed his work with a vehemence that was unusual even for him. He was spading the good earth like three men, and the air was loud with his huffing.

"I don't see why he has to go at it like a chicken with its head off," Pat murmured as I drove toward Washington University to drop Ted. "You know what'll happen—he'll simply exhaust himself."

"Oh, he'll slow down, now we're gone," I said. "He was just showing us. You know."

"But I don't like that gray look his face gets after he's been working too hard. Do you, Ted?"

Ted squirmed. "I'm not a doctor yet. But I know that when Dad's father was five years younger than he is now he died of a heart attack." I too had heard the story of how our grandfather had held his head under the pump spigot after a hard day's work and dropped dead of heart failure.

I stopped in front of the Big Bend Road gate to the campus. Ted remained sitting. None of us said anything for a few seconds. It was a lovely spring day, sunny and fragrant. "Dammit, it's our weekend too," I said at last.

"This weather's too nice to work," Ted said dully.

"Let's go back and get it over with," Pat said, and I turned the car around.

"We can be through by noon easy," I muttered.

As we reappeared in the driveway, Father straightened up like a jackknife snapping open, though he didn't quite make it; whenever he bent over for a while, his back stiffened. He stood thus, at half-mast, regarding us intently, his brows stern as we piled out of the car. "We're going to give you a hand with this," I said as we passed him to go inside and change to work clothes. He gave me a stony look. "We decided it's too nice a day to be indoors," I said carefully.

His eyes snapped. "You don't have to bother on my account. I'm doing all right." He was still spading the new yellow bed. I estimated he had about 80 per cent of the work still to do. I said I thought we'd take a lick at it, and he resumed his spading. "Suit yourselves," he said.

"There's gratitude," I said to my wife and brother as we entered the house. "You'd think we came back to borrow money from him."

"The way he acts," Pat said, "I'm not sure he'll even let us

help now," and Ted and I had to laugh. Though it was easy enough to make Father mad at us, he never got so foolish-mad as to refuse free labor.

We all changed and came marching down again. "Let's keep firmly in mind that we're doing him a special favor," I said. "Don't let him get the idea that this is going to be a regular thing." Pat and Ted nodded vigorously, and we descended upon Father.

Ted reached for the spade. "I'll finish this digg——" he said, but Father thrust the spade at me and said to Ted, "You can start pulling the old bushes out of the other three beds." He turned to Pat. "You load them into the wheelbarrow." He strode off to connect the hose. "Use gloves," he bawled back over his shoulder. "Thorns."

While we got gloves, he made five trips across the yard and into the basement for things, running part of the time. He always worked fast, and it was catching; we found ourselves hurrying. I got a march-time rhythm into the spading; Ted was yanking up ten rosebushes a minute, and Pat discovered she could get more into the wheelbarrow if she jumped up and down on them awhile first. Father began to look approvingly on this busy little scene as he sped by us from time to time, and presently he sent Ted off to dump the wheelbarrow load in a vacant area at the foot of the street where the river Des Peres flowed if there was any water in it. Pat helped unwrap and prune the new roses, and I mopped my face and started spading the new white-rose bed.

By noon and a hasty sandwich break it was plain that we would not finish so soon. What had seemed to be a few dozen new rosebushes turned out to be over a hundred, and Father was particular about how they should be planted, mounding up the earth at the bottom of each hole to spread the pruned roots, filling with a potting mixture that he had set Ted to blending in an old washtub, then dishing the surface of the ground around the bush and watering three times. Every bush seemed a major operation, and by three o'clock the pace of the help had slackened quite a bit. By four we felt like hissing the thirty or so bushes still remaining, and Ted regretted he had not taken a few along on each of his wheelbarrow excursions to the river Des Peres. But now Father was feeling the strain of the project too. Also, he was once more in perfect good humor with us all again. "We'll just heel the rest of them in," he said. "No use killing ourselves." He made a trench in the pink-rose bed-to-be, jabbed the leftover bushes into it, and heaped moist earth over them. "They'll keep fine till next week," he said, and started putting tools away.

The three of us looked at each other blankly. The day was shot. We were hungry and dirty and tired. Tomorrow our muscles would hurt from playing with Father's toys. "Well," I muttered hoarsely, "at least we have it almost done. What's left can't take more than a couple of hours next Saturday morning."

This estimate may have been right, but because of something Father did, we had no chance to find out. He said nothing about this until the following Saturday morning, and his reference even then was cryptic. "You go ahead and get started planting," he said to the rest of us while we were still at the breakfast table. "I'll be right back." He was dressed for public appearance.

"Probably off for another ton of fertilizer," Ted said, watching Father wiggle his car out of the driveway. "He's drunk with power." A prophetic remark. Almost as soon as we had got outside and started work to finish up the pesky job and be free, Father was back—and his car trunk was a thicket of rosebushes. More rosebushes. More new rosebushes.

"Westover Nurseries had a good buy on these," he said gaily, starting to haul them out. "Latest thing. Petals red outside and yellow inside, or maybe the other way around. I'll mark off a place for the new bed."

"Well?" I said privately to Pat and Ted. "Shall we quit now? You can see what's going to happen."

Pat shook her head. "There's nothing to worry about." Ted and I looked at her skeptically. Our experience had been that with Father there was always something to worry about. "After all," Pat said, pointing about her, "this is just a *yard*, not a farm or something. There simply isn't room for much more planting, and to all intents and purposes this load will finish it."

This common-sense point of view became plainer and plainer as the day and we wore on. There *wasn't* room for any more rose beds in the yard, or for much of anything else, unless Father switched to hanging gardens. Even he realized this. "I guess this just about does it," he said at the end of the day, regret tingeing his voice. "I'd had an idea——" He let it dangle, and none of us cared to ask what idea he'd had. He had had too many already. In fact, he had another one the very next day, and innocent as it seemed, we were as wary as cats about it. He sprang it right after our noon Sunday dinner.

"How about taking a ride with me?" he asked the three of us. We detected a plot; having enrolled us in part of his own weekend pattern, he was now trying for more. He would have liked nothing better than to be in complete control of all our spare time and effort—and, to give him credit, our rewards. Sensing now that the noes were about to carry the question by acclamation, he added quickly, "There's something I'd like very much to show you."

This was astute of him. Even though Ted and I were but little swayed, Pat's curiosity was quickened by Father's tone and by a mysterious little smile playing about his lips.

We all climbed into his car and he zoomed up the curving hill to Delmar Boulevard and headed west at his joy-ride pace, passing everything on the road and putting the fear into strolling dogs and pedestrians about to plunge off curbs. He aimed due west until he arrived at Lindbergh Boulevard, a main county highway, where he turned north. After two or three miles he swung into a side road and parked.

"This way," he said, getting out and climbing a five-foot bank of earth.

We scrambled up after him and found ourselves standing in a little field. Below us to the north the ground dropped sharply away into a ravine and then flattened out beyond in a swampy few acres skirted by tracks of the Creve Coeur streetcar line. "Like it?" Father said, flirting his hand about to indicate vast areas. "It's mine. Eighteen acres."

"Yours!" we said in one voice when we finally found it.

He nodded. "Part of it's on the other side of the highway," he said, shaking out a plat that showed the acreage as a nightmare of geometry. "Now let me show you something else." He strode off in a northeasterly direction down the field, and we tagged along through knee-high grasses. He was a secretive man in so many ways, you never knew what he was going to buy next. And he was always dabbling in real estate, feeling that he could make his fortune buying cheap and selling dear. So far it had worked fine the other way around.

"Right here," he said, coming to a halt in what seemed to be the one level spot in the entire territory, probably an acre or so in extent.

"A building site?" Pat asked tentatively. From time to time Father would speak of building a new house, in the way Ted and I had once spoken of becoming cowboys and Indians.

"An orchard!" Father cried triumphantly. We could hardly believe our ears. "Look at all the room," he exulted. "Why, you could drop our whole entire yard in here and lose it." Sounded like an excellent idea, I thought. We had now filled up the yard, but to fill up this great gob of land . . . ? I could hear Father's voice going on as he cited lush expectations—peaches, plums, grapes, apples, pears, raspberries, strawberries. . . .

He was holding, like a baton, a catalogue from Stark Brothers Nurseries, I saw, which he had been hiding in his inside pocket. I caught the eyes of my wife and brother, and like mine, theirs had a terribly frustrated look. Clearly, if you gave Father an inch, he would take an acre. Why—even six months, I told myself, is too long to give this fool household experiment. For Father is simply incurable. And pretty soon we'll be incurable, too, if we stay.

# 7. *Father and Sport*

Though she was the one usually in favor of giving any hopeless situation one more chance, Pat agreed with me now that things had gone from bad to worse and were trying for impossible. "The only way for us to get along with my father is to leave him," I said.

She nodded reluctantly. "I know what you mean."

"I don't mean he doesn't mean well. I guess he just can't help trying to run everybody else's life."

"Of course, he doesn't realize what he's gradually doing to us. He doesn't realize he's a dictator."

"Realize it or not," I said, "that's the way things are."

"What's up?" Ted said, coming upon us. "You two have a funny look."

"We think we may have to give this up as a bad job," I said. "Get our own home again."

"Then I think I'll come and live with you," he said. Pat and I blinked in unison. "It gets buggy around here with nobody but Dad and me," Ted said. "Real spotty."

He sauntered off, and Pat and I looked at each other. "Now

what?" I said. We didn't know. The idea of Father rattling
around the empty house, abandoned by all, disturbed us pro-
foundly. We decided to sleep on it a bit before we made a
move, and we did, and then, as with many problems you
duck, somebody else works them out.

The somebody else in this case was Dr. Raggler, our family
physician. It was a rare thing for Father to see the doctor,
and he went this time only because he had strained his bad
knee while working with the rosebushes and it was clicking
when he walked. The clicking made him edgy, and he was
afraid the knee might get so bad he couldn't drive a car, God
forbid. The doctor told him it would mend with the help of a
simple elastic support, and then while he had Father in his
clutches he took the opportunity to check on his health
generally and find out what he'd been doing. He was an out-
spoken man and had known Father for thirty-five years.
"Now, Ed," he said, "there's no use being a damn fool about
overexertion. You're not a kid any more. You go join a golf
club and exercise in moderation from now on."

The surprising thing was that Father took this so calmly.
Possibly the doctor had said something more than what he
reported. At any rate, he immediately dropped the orchard
project and got ready to begin the new life of sport and
leisure. He went about it in his usual manner, as if he were
killing hogs.

"First I'll have to buy some nice golf clothes if I'm going
to be playing at a club," he said, starting a list. "Some of
those plus-fours things, I guess."

"Not unless you want to look like Aunt Tilly at the Picnic,"
Ted said bluntly. "Those bloomers went out years ago." Father gazed at him under his eyebrows. "Take my word for
it," Ted said. "The campus fashion plates now wear slacks
on the golf course."

"Slacks," Father murmured, and wrote it down. He usually
paid no mind to anything Ted or I said about his clothes, but
this was strange territory for him.

"Now write down golf shoes," Ted said, "and wool socks, some sports shirts, and a jacket. A hat, too, something simple and sporty." Father wrote the things down. "That'll do for a starter," Ted said. "You've already got a bag of clubs." Father nodded, though not with his usual positiveness. His list was already finished and there was lots more paper. However, he did have a set of clubs. Years before, my maternal grandfather, an athletic man who was good at games, had taken up golf and then had rallied all his sons-in-law to take it up, too—as, when he had bought his first automobile, he had rapidly taught all the males in the family to drive. Father had learned to play golf, just as he had learned to drive, but he had never played enough to get out of the duffer class, and Grandfather could beat the pants off him.

He went downtown to Famous-Barr and got himself out-fitted by a salesman he knew in the men's department. The salesman always looked after Father, phoning him sometimes about bargains and putting aside things he thought would look well on him. He worked partly on commission and he was devoted to Father.

When he came home, Father had all the things Ted had specified, plus a few knickknacks such as sunglasses and a pocket pedometer that would show him how far he walked during a game of golf. He was especially taken with the pedometer and spent a good portion of the evening figuring out the exact length of his stride so he could set the little machine correctly.

"By the way," Ted said, "have you thought about some club you might join?" His tone faintly implied that perhaps no club would have Father.

"The Brookfield," Father said without a moment's hesitation. "Some of the men at the office belong." I knew the name of the club but not much else. I had almost no interest in golf and was even worse than Father at it.

"It's kind of a dump," Ted said, and Father bristled. "I went to a dance there once," Ted said.

"I'm not going there to dance," Father shouted. "And any-way, it's a very high-class club. No tipping, and you can have a drink or something alongside the swimming pool after the game." But even Father's drinking, I thought, was not keyed to clubby sport. Whisky was the only hard liquor he knew, and he used it mainly in toddies when he had a cold. "I'd better have a look at my clubs," he said suddenly, and hurried upstairs. He kept them in his bedroom clothes closet, which was a kind of small storehouse for all sorts of things, whether he used them every day or once in his life. He came downstairs lugging the canvas bag and frowning. "Kind of shabby," he said, holding the bag out. "With all my new clothes——"

"Not a thing wrong with that bag," Ted said. "All the boys use beat-up bags." Father winced. "Casual—that's the idea," Ted said. "And why drag around ten pounds of leather?"

Father poked among his clubs. He had three irons and two woods. Grandfather always declared it was the man, not the clubs, and had offered to play any of his duffer sons-in-law using only a midiron against their bagful for a dollar a hole. Father went off to the basement with his paltry set of clubs, and when he came back the irons were gleaming from a steel-wool buffing and from the bag came a powerful fragrance. "Furniture polish," he said as we sniffed hard. "I gave all the shanks a good soaking."

"They'll smell you coming three holes ahead," Ted said in a stifled voice. "Air those things all night or you're a marked man."

"Smell all right to me," Father muttered, but he put the clubs on the back porch to spend the night.

When he came back, Pat had thought of something. "Aren't you going to put your new golf clothes on to show us, Dad?" she asked. Usually he paraded any new clothes as soon as he got them.

"Oh . . . you'll see them tomorrow," he said vaguely. "They're just . . . clothes."

They were, but on Father they were revolutionary—tan flannel slacks with pleats, brown suède jacket, yellow golf

shoes, checked sports shirt, and a soft canvas hat that looked
like a mashed potato on his head. He twitched as he con-
fronted us. "The man at Famous," he began defensively,
"said this——"

"You look all right around the head," Ted said. "The rest
of the outfit needs a lot of weathering." Father stepped in
front of the living-room Venetian mirror and took a peek at
himself. He hastily turned away. "You're not supposed to
wear those shoes inside," Ted added. "You keep them in your
locker."

Father looked down at his hobnailed shoes. He yanked
them off and went upstairs again, in his wool-sock feet, his
air suddenly definite. He was down in ten minutes, dressed
as if for the office, and looking relieved. In his hand he carried a small satchel. "I'll just carry my golfing things," he
said firmly, and marched out.

He didn't tell us what the club dues were or very much
of anything else about the establishment. Apparently he
wanted to get thoroughly familiar with the new environment
first. "What did you shoot?" Ted asked when he came home
the first time, but he had torn up his score card and said
he didn't remember but that he had walked three and two-
tenths miles. He had played with three chemists from his
office, Harvard graduates who spoke a common patois, and
we could tell that things could have been better. "It's more
what he doesn't say," I told Pat, "than what he does."

"You know what I think?" she said suddenly. "I think he's
running into a bunch of clubby snobs."

"But that wouldn't bother him," I said. "He's got too good
an opinion of himself."

"It'd bother me," she said shortly. I thought I knew what
Father's trouble was but I decided to keep it to myself for
the time being and see if it proved out. It began to, the very
next weekend.

He came home from the club with a spring in his step.
"Very interesting day," he said. "I had a fine time."

"What score?" Ted asked.

"I didn't play," Father said. "Doc Allan said it might be a good idea to get a few pointers from the club professional." He looked hard at us. "Keeps you up to date. Styles change in golf."

"What'd he teach you?" Ted asked.

"Oh, lots of things," Father said. "He's got a nice little shop there, too, and I bet you can't guess what he grosses per annum." None of us tried. "Twenty-five thousand dollars," Father cried. "And it isn't any bigger than this room."

"What'd he try to sell you?" Ted inquired.

"Nothing," Father said. "He loaned me a matched set of clubs, beautiful things. I may buy them."

"I see," Ted said. "How much?"

"Oh, and I bought a new bag," Father said, skipping nimbly aside. "Brown saddle leather." He looked coolly at Ted. "The pro said it would outlast canvas ten to one."

He did buy the clubs, the following week, and gradually picked up other accessories of the game, brought to his attention by his association with the club professional. In a month or so he was the best equipped non-playing golfer in the area. "Another thing," he said, "there's practically no overhead in the shop. The club supplies the space and so on."

"You're talking about the club pro again?" I said.

"Yes, sure. And of course there's no deterioration to speak of on the stock, either."

"Is he teaching you anything about golf?" I asked.

"All kinds of things. My slice is gone."

"I suppose you'll begin playing again, then?"

"I suppose," he said. "I mean yes, of course. Certainly."

I doubted this but perhaps I underestimated Father's sense of values. Services of the club pro were not cheap, I was sure, and there was only one way to get your money's worth out of them. Father rejoined his office partners and played ball again. If he did so now with a kind of doggedness, at least he did so more skillfully than before. He went around nine holes in fewer than fifty strokes, and though he declined to make side bets, he was willing to buy or accept a drink afterwards on the basis of best score. He was against gambling but apparently he did not count this, which was lucky for us as it turned out; it put into our hands a persuader to use on Father soon afterwards.

For, to put it briefly, Father's interest in golf was rapidly dwindling. He was now playing as if it were a duty and to realize something on his outlay. Ted and I saw the symptoms, though Pat as yet did not. "It certainly makes a difference, having Dad out of the house on Saturdays," she said. "Especially after that rosebush business."

"Enjoy it while it lasts," I said, and she looked alarmed. "He's not the playboy type, is he, Ted?"

"He hates to waste time," Ted said, "except ours. We'll have him on our backs again in a month."

It didn't take a month. It took only a week, and I suppose I was partly responsible. If I had kept quiet, Father would have kept on going to the club at least long enough to learn what he thought was one of the bartender's dearest secrets. He came home in a pleasant glow even though he had played the kind of round that made him tear up his score card. "Had a wonderful new drink," he told us. "I can't remember now what they call it, but it had whisky and there was a cherry and a slice of orange and some kind of good flavoring."

"Served in a low, wide glass?" I asked.

"Yes. I'm going to try and get the directions. But I'm afraid a man wouldn't let go of a good thing like that."

"Sounds like an old-fashioned," I said. Father stared at me. He knew surprisingly little about mixed drinks. What drinking he did was mostly at home and most of that was of his own homemade wine. "That's the name!" he cried after a moment of stunned silence. "How did *you* know?" He had never quite convinced himself that I had become old enough to drink, vote, or smoke cigars.

"I've had them," I said. "A little sweet for my taste, but I can make them for you if you like."

"You know how to *make* them?" Father gasped. "Are you sure?"

"I could make you one right now if we had some bitters. You don't really need the fruit, and we've got whisky and sugar in the house."

Father yanked out his wallet. "Here," he said, handing me a five-dollar bill. "Buy everything you need. Everything. Cherries and oranges, and I think there was pineapple too."

I got the works, including swizzle sticks and some authentic old-fashioned glasses, and mixed him a sample drink when I got home. He sipped it. "By George," he exclaimed, "it's the same thing." He settled back in his easy chair, looking more relaxed than he had in weeks. From the kitchen wafted the aroma of lamb chops broiling. "Now this," Father said, "is more like it." He took another sip of the drink and gave it a dreamy stir with the swizzle stick. "To tell you the truth," he said, "golf takes up an awful lot of a man's time."

From the kitchen Pat overheard the remark. "Well, you've certainly fixed us up now," she hissed when I stepped out there. "He won't have any reason at all to go to that club. We're right back where we started." We certainly were. And with Father taking it easier on doctor's orders, he could spend more time planning things he wanted us to do. "And I," Pat said, "do not intend to spend *my* whole summer grubbing in the earth."

"Guess we'll have to have that showdown after all——" I said, and stopped. Father was coming out to the kitchen.

"Time for another one before dinner?" he inquired pleasantly, holding up his empty glass. He looked as relaxed as warm spaghetti. It was rare indeed for him to have his mind on anything but dinner at this hour.

"Why, yes, Dad," Pat said after a moment. "Yes—plenty of time." He went back to the living room humming, and I fixed the drink. "Maybe this isn't such a bad thing at that," Pat murmured, watching me. "I'm getting an idea." She told me what it was. "I'll spring it on him at the table, after his

second drink," she said. "I think that's psychologically sounder."

It was. By then Father was sounding so mellow I would hardly have known him in the dark. "Have you noticed how many people around here are using their back yards for recreation?" Pat remarked at dinner.

"Say, that sounds interesting," Father said. "What are they doing in them?"

She told him what we had noticed in strolls around the neighborhood—badminton, shuffleboard, darts, and so on. "We ought to do something with our yard," she murmured.

"Yes. Too bad there isn't any room," I said on cue.

Father gave me a calm look. "If there isn't any room," he said airily, "we'll make room." Pat smiled. I smiled. Ted smiled. "Sport at home," Father said. "Now *that* makes good sense."

After some discussion we settled on croquet, a game Pat had learned to play like a swooping hawk when she was a child. It was a compromise but an acceptable compromise. That summer we had to spend a good deal of time at home playing croquet with Father, but it beat playing with rosebushes. He found his golf clothes just the thing for the game too. And whenever we needed a good jolting argument on almost any subject thereafter, I mixed him an old-fashioned before we discussed it.

# 8. *Father's Sacred Closet*

At this point in our household experiment my wife did my father a great favor. She did it to please herself, but he assumed it was mostly on his account. She quit her job. She had found that keeping house for three men was quite a job in itself, and after riding home from work with Father each evening for a good while, she felt her nerves were going. Since he didn't know it, none of this bothered Father and he could now stop biting his tongue whenever he started to criticize married women who held outside jobs. Like most of the men of his generation, he opposed the practice as against nature and the will of God. Money, we could have told him, also had something to do with it; had I not changed jobs myself at about this time, Pat would probably have kept on working, but my new job, with the advertising department of a utility company, paid more than newspaper work.

It was also a great comfort to Father that I was now working in an office instead of a newsroom. Offices he understood. All in all he seemed on the threshold of better times at home, so that it came as a shock when he learned that one of the first things Pat planned to do was to clean house.

"It looks clean enough to me," he said. "Katy keeps after it." Katy, as a matter of fact, had been so well indoctrinated by Father on how he felt about an upset house that she could make the rounds of the rooms with a feather duster and leave no evidence that she had been near them.

"The whole entire house has to be gone over," Pat said firmly. "But I'll do it with as little upset as possible—a room a day." Though this was going to mean an entire week of housecleaning, Father took heart from her air of command. She began the task on Monday, and when he got home that evening he thought she had changed her mind. "Not at all," she said. "We cleaned the sunroom today."

"Good," he said, inspecting it. "Looks exactly the same as it did." He meant it as a compliment, and as Pat and Katy worked their way through the house in this fashion it bothered Father so little that by the time they got to his bedroom he was not at all alarmed. In former years he had sometimes had to sleep on the sofa for a night, so massive was the upheaval of housecleaning. His bedroom was due for its workout on Saturday, and not having seen Pat and Katy in action, he had planned to spend the day at home.

Right after breakfast Pat began organizing buckets and washing powder and was wrapping an old piece of sheet around the broom bristles when Father noticed it and asked what it was for. "To sweep the walls and ceiling," she said, and filled a bucket with hot water. The steamy smell of washday billowed through the kitchen, and Father recoiled. "Woodwork," Pat said. She wet a chamois cloth. "Windows," she remarked, and poured some vinegar into another bucket. An old haunted look crept into Father's eyes. "If you need anything out of your room, Dad," she said briskly, "you'd better get it now, before we start——"

"Give me five minutes," he said, and shot upstairs.

Katy gazed after him and muttered something. "She said she hopes he stays away till we're good and finished with his room," Pat said when I asked for a translation. Katy spoke in a machine-gun version of English I couldn't catch, but I could understand how she felt; she wanted to be sure the lion was out if she had to walk into his den, let alone clean it.

Father left the house, holding his breath as he sped through the steamy kitchen. "Don't bother about lunch for me," he called from the porch. "I won't be back till it's over."

Ted and I volunteered to clean the basement, and for a while things were peaceful. The housecleaning on the second floor was so far away it seemed hardly to exist. We made an electromagnet from a hunk of soft iron and were testing its pickup power when we heard Pat through the clothes chute, an expensive refinement that served solely as an intercom system. She sounded mildly irritated, and we went up to see, expecting to help move something heavy. As we stepped into the bedroom, into the teeth of a breeze howling through the flung-up windows, Katy directed a volley of words at us. Pat twitched her head impatiently. "She says nobody ever touches Dad's closet." Katy worked her head up and down. "Does he clean it himself?" Pat demanded of us.

"He doesn't let it get dirty," Ted finally said, and I nodded.

Pat marched into the closet. "You call this clean?" she demanded, extending a finger tip. Katy shuddered. Pat accidentally bumped the closet door and we all ducked out of habit. On the inside of the door was a loose-hanging shelf arrangement of thin boards and ropes, and when Father opened the door too quickly they hit him. He stored hat and shoes in current use there. Katy began sidling toward the door to the hall. "All right—you don't have to have anything to do with it," Pat said, and Katy dashed downstairs to scrub the porches. "You can give me a hand instead," Pat said to Ted and me.

"Just what," I said carefully, "do you propose to do?" The closet was shaped like a huge wedge; there were three

clothes poles, the front one at normal height and the others
stepping lower to follow the slant ceiling, and each was
jammed with Father's clothing. His shoes covered most of
the visible floor space; his hats were stacked on the broad
shelf, and his oddments of ties, umbrellas, and golf clubs
filled all remaining space.

"I'm going to clean it," Pat said, and disappeared into the
closet. There was a sound of wrestling and she reappeared,
breathing hard and holding a blue serge suit coat on a
hanger. "He's got enough clothes for ten men," she said, and
held out the coat. "Just lay this on the bed. We'll stack them
there."

Ted and I put our hands in our pockets. "I think we'd
better talk this over," I said to my wife. "There's nothing
to talk over," she said, laying the coat on the bed herself.
"I have to empty the closet to clean it." She yanked out
a pair of Father's spare trousers and a hat and spread them
on the bed. The arrangement of the hat, coat, and pants
looked a little like Father on the bed, perhaps after an en-
counter with a street roller. I averted my eyes.

"I think I'd better go study," Ted murmured, edging toward the door.

"You two make me tired," Pat said. "You can just stay here
and help. Anybody as neat as your father would *want* his
closet cleaned." She handed out a few suits and an overcoat,
and I took them with a sigh and spread them on the bed.

"If you're bound and determined to commit this," I said,
"let's get it over with fast. Let me in there and I'll hand the
stuff out to Ted and he can stack it." I took her place in the
closet and began handing things out.

"How much more?" she asked after a while. "Have you
got the first pole cleared?" I nodded from the closet doorway. "What's the matter?" she cried. "Can't you talk?"

I stuck my head out. "I was holding my breath," I said.
"This closet even smells like Father—sort of soapy. It makes
me nervous being here like this."

"I wouldn't have believed all this could come out of there," Pat said, looking at the final heap of suits, pants, overcoats, shoes, hats, and miscellaneous items. "Hasn't he ever thrown away anything?"

"Not often," I said, "and when he has, I've usually got it, so it stayed in the family." Among the shoes were two pairs of high-top button ones in good condition. By nesting his older hats he had been able to accommodate fifteen on the shelf. "It's this way," I said. "He buys a hat and a pair of shoes and maybe two suits each year. But he's easy on his clothes, so the old ones are always too good to throw out."

"Couldn't he give them to the Salvation Army?"

"He has a block about that. He'll donate money but he feels personal about his clothes."

"Lookee here," Ted said, and held out a box of stiff collars, the high ones we used to call Herbert Hoover collars.

"Now those," Pat declared passionately, "can certainly be thrown out."

Ted and I shook our heads in perfect time. "You may not believe this," I said, "but Father knows by heart every last thing in his closet. One time I needed a velvet smoking jacket for a play I was in, and he came up here and got——"

"Just a minute," Pat said. "He doesn't wear smoking jackets. In fact, that's one thing he doesn't have in this mare's-nest."

"He wore them when he was a young man. And he doesn't have any now because after the play they all got lost or something. He loaned me a green one, a red one, and a striped one, and he was quite upset when they disappeared. Said there was still lots of wear in them."

She wagged her head numbly, and Ted and I helped her wash down the emptied closet so Father's things could be hustled back in. He and I found ourselves glancing out the front windows now and then; we were so used to having Father show up at the worst times that we had believed in mental telepathy before we knew there was such a thing. But instead of whisking things back in as soon as the closet was

ready, Pat calmly began sorting out the wool clothing.
"These things should be dry-cleaned to discourage moths,"
she said, "now that the closet is clean."

"No moths in there," I said. "Let's get the stuff back."

"I didn't *see* any moths, but it stands to reason——"

I shook my head. "He brings home cans of paradichloro-
benzene from work, and the fumes——"

"Cans of *what?*"

"One of the chemicals they make. Any moth fool enough
to go into that closet is a goner. Anyway, he has his clothes
cleaned regularly." I started stuffing things back into the
closet as Ted handed them over. We were going like an assembly line while Pat still hovered restlessly over the dwindling stack, when suddenly she pounced and hoisted aloft
an olive-drab ensemble. "What in heaven's name is this?"
she cried.

I told her it was his old Home Guard uniform; the Home
Guards were the Civilian Defense of World War I. "They
drilled and paraded," I said, "and had rifle practice, in case
the Kaiser sent a Zeppelin over to capture St. Louis." She
took the uniform to the window to see it better. The jacket
buttoned all the way to the stand-up collar, and the pants
were breeches that laced up and had canvas leggings to go
over them. In one of the hatboxes there was an old Army
hat, wide-brimmed, with a crown shaped like a tent.

"Does he ever wear this costume?" she asked at last.

"Well, no," I said, "but don't think for a minute he doesn't
want to keep it."

"Does he have it cleaned?" she asked.

"Why would he have it cleaned? If he doesn't wear——"

"Then it has to be cleaned," she said. "After all," she added
firmly, "he could go camping in it if it was nice and clean."

Father was as likely to go camping as he was to take up
zither playing, but I didn't want to spend the rest of the
day on the uniform question. "Send it, send it," I said. "Now
let's jam the rest of his stuff back in here."

Father took the rape of his closet less hard than I had expected. When he came charging out of it after one shocked look, he was not foaming at the mouth, and his volume was no more than double normal as he bawled: "What happened in here?"

"I cleaned it, Dad," Pat said, leaving Ted and me well out of it.

"Cleaned it?" he repeated woodenly. My mother had never offered to clean it and had frequently declared she wouldn't touch it with a ten-foot pole.

"It's all nice and straight now," Pat said, a remark that must have seemed wildly exaggerated to Father, because he set to work at once to rearrange things in the exact order they had been before; I had not paid much attention to such fine details while stowing the stuff back in. In the course of this rearranging he justified what I had said about his memory.

"My Home Guard uniform," he cried, bolting out of the closet. "It's gone."

"I sent it to the cleaners," Pat said, and his mouth slowly opened. "So it won't be a moth breeder," she added. She looked at him more closely, up and down. "But now . . . I'm not so sure you can still——"

Father's stomach abruptly became flatter, and his chest rose. His heels clicked slightly and he pulled his chin in, giving him quite a jowly look. "My weight's been practically the same since I was twenty-five years old," he said in clipped tones. "It was all right to send my uniform to be cleaned, as long as they're careful with it. You never know when you'll need a thing like that, and it's good to have it ready."

The uniform came back the following week. The cleaners had done a surprisingly good job, I thought, as if they had been dealing with a valuable antique, and Father seemed pleased, too, when he slipped the protective paper bag off to look at the result. "They don't make clothes like this today," he said. "Feel that material, look at that color. Not a bit faded."

Ted kept looking from the uniform to Father and back again. He was too young to remember what Father had looked like in it. "How about putting it on?" he said at last.

"Well, I hate to wrinkle it," Father said, patting the coat.

"You actually buttoned that thing all the way up?" Ted said. "Without throttling yourself?"

"It's a uniform," Father cried. "It has to fit trim and snug and—oh, all right, I'll show you." He marched off upstairs to his bedroom with the uniform over his arm. "Wear the hat too," Ted called after him. "I want to get the whole picture."

"Speaking of pictures," I said after we had been waiting for a few minutes, "I remember one of him in that uniform." I got up and opened one of the drawers of Father's secretary-desk where he kept old photographs. "Yep," I said, "here's a snapshot of him at camp." It showed Father and his squad in front of a tent. He looked militant and slender, in good fighting trim. "Well, there's our Before shot," I said. "Now, if we could get an After——"

"I'll see if I can borrow Mr. Gorset's camera," Ted said, dashing out. "Tell Dad to wait." The Gorsets were our neighbors on the south. Ted was back in a few minutes, breathless but empty-handed. "No film," he said. "Where is he?"

"I guess he's being extra particular," I said. There were a couple of thumps from upstairs and then several more, as if Father was skipping rope in his sock feet. Ted and Pat and I looked at the vibrating ceiling. "Do you suppose he's forgotten how to put it on?" Pat said.

Before I could answer, I heard Father's voice coming hoarsely from the stair well. "Ken," he was yelling, "can you come up here a minute?"

I went up. He was in his bedroom and halfway in his Home Guard breeches. He was taking deep and quivering breaths, and I noticed that his uniform coat, lying on the bed, was now ripped at both shoulder seams. "Never mind

that," he said when he saw me staring at it. "Help me get out of these damned pants." The breeches looked a good deal like long underwear, and they fit Father like a coat of paint, as far as he had got. He thudded down on the bed and held out one leg, and I tried to work off that leg of the breeches.

"I can't catch hold of anything," I said. "How'd you ever get them on so tight?"

"By jumping," he snapped, and wiggled his feet nervously. "I haven't got any feeling in them. Good Lord—they've stopped the circulation. Hurry up." I tried the other leg, without luck. Father yanked the top of the breeches down and sat on the floor. "Try to peel 'em off," he said. I began yanking. "Wait," he howled after a few seconds of this. "You're dragging me." He scooted back to the starting place and got a good grip on one leg of his bed by winding his arms around it behind him. "Go," he said, and I started peeling again.

"It's your knees," I said presently, between tugs. "They must be pretty knobby. The breeches are hung up there, and I can't seem to——"

"Stop," Father roared. "The bed's coming too." Sure enough, the heavy bed was inching along with each pull. Father sat on the floor, panting, for a few moments. "Get Ted," he then muttered, and I called down the stair well. "Now," Father said when Ted appeared, "one of you brace yourself in my closet doorway and hold me under my arms, and the other one pull on the breeches."

"Which end do you want?" I said to Ted. He was looking hard at Father's legs, which resembled sausages in their casings. "Hurry up," Father cried at him. "You're studying medicine. You ought to know I could get gangrene from this."

"Hold still," Ted said. He fetched a razor blade. "Routine accident procedure," he said, ripping the breeches from Father's legs. They flopped to the floor, and after a startled moment Father began to massage his legs with much tenderness.

I gathered up the ruined breeches and picked the burst

coat off the bed. "What do you want to do with——" I began.

"You know what the trouble was?" Father said suddenly from the floor. "Civilian cleaners don't know how to clean military clothing. They shrank the daylights out of my good uniform. It should've been sent to a military cleaner, somebody who handles the work at Jefferson Barracks."

"Jefferson Barracks," I said. "That's where the Home Guards trained, isn't it?"

"We bivouacked there," Father said, sounding much snappier, "between maneuvers."

"As a matter of fact," I said, "I just ran across an old snapshot of you when you were there. It was in your desk with a lot of other old pictures." He had started to get off the floor, but he sank down again. "You looked good in your uniform," I said, "but I don't think they were feeding you very well at the barracks."

"No," Ted said. "You looked a lot skinn——"

"I've got to give that desk a good cleaning out," Father said heavily, getting to his feet. He glanced at the ruptured Home Guard uniform, which I was still holding, awaiting his pleasure. "Throw it away," he muttered. "I've already got too much old—too much stuff around here already."

# 9. *Father and the Aluminum Salesman*

In his own eyes Father was a good neighbor. He defined a good neighbor as one who took care of his house and yard and kept his nose out of other people's business. He was on an arm's-length bowing and chatting acquaintance with his own neighbors, and he had taken it for granted that everybody knew this would continue to be the household policy when Pat and I moved in with him. He was right, until Pat quit her job to stay home and keep house full time. When this happened she suddenly had the leisure to get acquainted with the people next door, and being young and friendly, she did so. At first Father didn't realize what was going on, and he might never have realized the extent it could reach if Madge Gorset hadn't gone to something called an aluminum dinner. From that moment on he was a marked man.

Madge came home from the dinner, given at some friend's house, full of enthusiasm for having one at her own home. She explained the deal to Pat.

"This aluminum salesman does every bit of the work. He brings the food and cooks it and even cleans up afterward, and you can invite all your friends and everybody gets some kind of a little present and it's loads of fun. You'll come, won't you?"

"Certainly," said Pat, who had got used to Madge's conversation. "Let me know when, so I can arrange things at home."

"It's tonight," Madge said.

"Tonight!" said Pat in a croak. "Oh, my." It was then mid-afternoon. "But I have to cook dinner for the boys and their father."

"Oh, they're included in the invitation," Madge said. "I need a crowd."

Pat thought of Father. "Well-l-l," she said.

"I'm counting on you, remember," Madge said, leaving. "If I don't have enough people I won't get a free orange juicer."

I got home a few minutes before Father, and Pat hastily briefed me. "He'll go, won't he?" she asked.

"If he does, it'll be the first time," I said.

"I wonder what's the best way to tell him?" she said, as if talking to herself.

"You won't have to tell him. He'll want to know why you're not cooking dinner, and that'll spill the beans." The wheels of Father's car were heard on the driveway gravel. "Quick," Pat cried. "Mix an old-fashioned. And don't hold the whisky."

By the time Father hit the back porch I had the drink mixed, and Pat thrust it at him as he came inside. He was so pleasantly surprised, he didn't remember to sniff the air in the kitchen. He took his drink into the living room and Pat followed and took his hat and coat and handed him the evening paper. "Well, well," he said. "Nothing like getting home from a hard day at the office and spending a nice restful evening."

"Oh yes," Pat warbled, glancing secretly at the mantel clock. We were due at the Gorsets' in ten minutes. "Is your drink all right, Dad?"

"Perfect," he said. "By the way, the Gorsets must be having

a party. Several cars in front. I could hardly get in my driveway, the way some idiot had parked."

"Oh?" Pat murmured.

"I guess he couldn't see to back up," Father said. "Whole
back seat of the fool car was full of pots and pans and—
what's the matter?"

"Just something in my throat," Pat said, and scurried back
to the kitchen, beckoning to me. "Mix him another," she
whispered, "before I tell him."

"One's his usual limit before dinner. Anyway, he'll get
suspicious."

She shrugged helplessly and marched back to confront Father who was sipping along, a third through his drink. "By
the way," he said, sounding mellow, "what are we having
for dinner, Pat?"

She hesitated for just a moment. "I'm not sure," she said
then. Father set his glass down and craned his neck to look
up at her from his deep easy chair. She took a long breath.
"I mean, we're going out for dinner, Dad."

"Out?" Father said blankly. "Not to Liz and Dean's? That's
next week, isn't it?" He referred to his two half sisters, who
had asked us to their house the following week. They were
his closest relatives in St. Louis.

"Not there," Pat said. "To a friend's house. And it's no trip
at all. It's just next door—it's the Gorsets."

"The *Gorsets!*" Father exclaimed after a three-second silence. "They're not friends. They're neighbors."

"Anyway, they asked us," Pat said hastily, "and I said we'd
come—and it's almost time."

Father sat like a rock. "The *Gorsets*," he said slowly. "I've
never been in their house. They've never been in my house.
I don't even know what the inside of their house *looks* like."

"It looks all right," Pat said, "and we have to leave in . . .
two minutes. If you'd like to wash your hands . . ."

Father suddenly picked up his glass and drained his old-
fashioned. "Two minutes," he muttered, and handed his glass

to Pat. "That's enough time for another. Never mind the ice and fruit."

While he gulped his second drink Pat rounded up Ted and then got everybody outside and aimed for the Gorset house. Halfway there Father stopped short, though a tasty smell of cooking beef was wafting from their kitchen. "We're not going in the *back* door?" he said hoarsely.

"Well," Pat said, "that's the way I always——"

He executed a column right oblique the Home Guards would have been proud of, a maneuver that took him firmly to the Gorsets' front door, with the rest of his squad bringing up the rear. Madge, who was expecting us at the kitchen door, had to run back through the house to open the front door, and Father spent the waiting time staring at the front-porch ceiling, which needed painting.

There were four other guests, two couples who were strangers to us, and to accommodate everyone chairs were arranged in an oval in the living room. Conversation died as we entered; we were introduced, and Father sat down with a trapped look. The Gorset house had just a nook for a dining room, and I wondered if Madge planned to feed us in shifts. Al, her husband, was quite a bit younger than Father, and while not tongue-tied in a crowd, he hadn't had much practice on Father. "We were talking about wrestling," he said, clearing his throat, "just before you came in."

Father looked startled. "Wrestling!" he exclaimed, darting glances about the room.

"Uh—wrestling *matches,*" Al said. "Professional wrestling, you know. At the Arena."

"Oh," Father said. "Those things. They're fakes." His tone suggested he wasn't there to waste time talking about fakes. The subject died, and the males of the party sat mute while the women chatted among themselves. I could hear Madge saying the dinner was just a demonstration and no one should feel they had to buy any aluminum just because they ate the man's food. Father was paying no attention; it was the sort of chatter he was used to ignoring. Across the oval from him a man who looked as if he sold bonds for a living gave Father the eye. "Kraft?" he said. "You related to the cheese people?"

It was a question Father was sick and tired of hearing. "No," he said in a loud voice, and the bond salesman clammed up. The other male stranger, a cowed-looking man with bags under his eyes, rubbed his jaw, opened his mouth, and then closed it for good. I began to think Father was kind of a wet blanket on the crowd.

"By the way, Al," I said for the sake of sociability, "what brand aluminum does this guy sell?" From the kitchen we could hear some heavy clatter every now and then. "It sounds solid enough," I added.

Father, sitting beside me, turned in his chair to stare better. "What'd you say?" he asked in a startled tone.

"Wondered what brand he represents." I saw I wasn't getting through. "Man who's cooking our dinner," I said. "The fellow in the kitchen."

Father shot a look in the direction of the kitchen, which was around two or three corners. For the first time he seemed to realize that this dinner party was different; instead of being out there slaving over a hot stove, the hostess was in here. And in the kitchen a salesman, of all things, was cooking dinner. Father seemed to rise a couple of inches in his chair, and I wondered if he was going to take off like a rocket for home. Al, looking nervous, spoke: "It's just kind of a gimmick, you know—just to get people to know the merchandise. Doesn't mean a thing." Father stared at him as bird at snake. "Very informal," Al said, stretching his neck as if his collar was suddenly too tight. "No obligation at all." Father did not reply. "And the food's pretty good, too . . ." Al finished, sounding like a wind-up record player running down.

If Father intended to leave, he was foiled, for at that moment a slight and surprisingly dapper young man wearing a regimental tie popped into the room and rapidly laid aluminum trays in our laps. The dining-room space problem was

solved; we were going to eat right where we were. "Like a picnic," Pat murmured, with a fleeting glance at Father who was sitting like a rock. When he went on a picnic he went to Forest Park, where there were picnic tables. While he was still glaring at the tray on his lap the young man zipped around our oval again, putting spoons and cups of a fruit cocktail on the trays, shot off to the kitchen again, and was back in a few moments. Unfolding a small stand, he stood behind it and began explaining the use of some aluminum gadget he had done something to the fruit with. Father laid down his spoon, waiting for the salesman to finish. "Go on and eat," I said from the corner of my mouth. "He won't mind." After another half minute Father took my advice, but the salesman was very pleased by his attention and addressed most of the remarks to him personally before he whizzed off to bring back the main course. When I saw what it was, I wondered what Father had done in his past life to deserve this evening.

"Is this . . . *pot* roast?" he muttered to me as the salesman took his station behind the little table and everybody else began eating.

"I'm not real sure," I said, but I was sure enough. I liked pot roast all right, but Father associated it with his youth. When he dined at his sisters' home he had to eat it or something like it, but he usually managed to avoid it everywhere else. "Tastes fine," I whispered, "and did you hear what the man just said? Said he cooked it on top of the stove, in that thing he's holding up."

"I don't care if he cooked it on top of his head," Father hissed, "if it's pot roast . . ." He paused, jabbing his fork at the vegetables. "Are these . . . *parsnips?*" he inquired in an escaping-steam voice. He chivied them about his plate. He had always treated parsnips as if they were a conspiracy against him.

"Well, the others are carrots," I said. "I'm sure of that much. Man says he cooked them right along with the roast on top of the stove and retained all the vital juices and valuable food elements." Father looked as if I was making it up. "I'm listening with one ear," I said. "Newspaper training."

He pushed the parsnips away off to the far edge of his plate and began eating the meat and carrots with the air of a man offered a choice of shooting or hanging. The salesman immediately began concentrating on him again, and I remembered hearing somewhere that it was good selling technique to pick someone in a crowd to talk to directly. The salesman was a good talker, but I felt he needed more practice in picking. Everyone except Father said the food was delicious. He said nothing and ate only enough to keep body and soul together, but he did look a little hopeful when our young man gathered up the plates and said he had angelfood cake for dessert. Father could almost make a meal of angel-food cake, and almost any icing suited him as long as it was good and thick.

The aluminum salesman hurried back, bearing his cake, and all the women drew in their breaths in admiration. The cake had risen perfectly, and not only that—like the pot roast, it had been baked on the top of the stove, the man announced. This produced another sensation among the cake-baking part of the audience but not from Father. "Do you mean to tell me," he asked me in a heavy undertone, "that that thing isn't *iced?*"

It certainly wasn't. "Bare as a baby," I said.

"Do have some, sir," said the salesman, dumping a slice lovingly on Father's tray. "Notice the texture. All done on top of the stove—not in the oven—on the Super Trio Combination Unit right there on my stand."

Father looked sourly at the combination unit, as if he was wondering what the sense was in not using an oven when it was there to be used. Nobody suggested this, however, and while the cake was being eaten the young man shook out a whole sample case of aluminum cooking things he hadn't mentioned yet and passed them around the oval and displayed them on the rug. They were all made of heavy aluminum and guaranteed to trap all the hormones and enzymes and things the food had and defend health in nature's own way, the young man said, and you could throw away your medicine bottles. It put me in mind of a revival meeting, but no converts came forward to buy any aluminum and the salesman lowered his sights a little. He put some of the frill items back in his case and whooped it up harder for the rest, but there still were no takers. By now we were all finished with the cake and Father was looking at the Gorsets' clock as if he was trying to make sure it was running.

The salesman made one more pitch after putting everything back in his case except a group of five or six utensils he declared were the absolute, irreducible minimum for abundant health. I felt a little sorry for him; it reminded me of some house-to-house selling I had done some years before. Everybody in this crowd plainly regarded it as a social gathering, tipped off by Madge. Everybody, that is, but Father. And he suddenly seemed to sense the situation. I could tell by the way he straightened up and stared around at the others, a flush creeping up the back of his neck. "Pat," he said abruptly, "could you use these things?" He pointed to the basic set of aluminum spread out on the rug, and Pat's eyes widened. Now that she was home, she was doing quite a lot of cooking. "Well, of course, I'd like——" she began, and it was enough.

"Wrap 'em up," he said to the young man, and got to his feet. He cast a dry glance at the company in general and drew out his wallet. "How much?" he said, pulling out a ten-dollar bill.

"Exactly thirty-five dollars and sixty-two cents, sir, including tax," said the young man breathlessly, "and thank *you.*"

"Thirt——" Father said, and got out his checkbook instead. "Well, let's get these gathered up," he said to Ted and me, and with this airtight excuse to leave we were all back home in no time.

"Dad, it was terribly sweet of you to buy them," Pat said

to him, "but I hope you don't think I asked you to go with that in mind."

Father shook his head. He opened the icebox and looked searchingly in. "Certainly not," he said, selecting a drumstick, some olives, and a wedge of cheese. He ate them standing, as if he was starving. "If there's one thing I can't stand," he said presently, "it's looking cheap." He glanced restlessly around and then went to the hall closet and explored the end of the upper shelf, which was reserved for his use. He came back unwrapping a box of chocolates, passed them around, and ate about ten himself in rapid succession. He usually had some candy stashed away for emergencies.

"Well, you certainly didn't look cheap," Pat said. "Thirty-five dollars——"

"I'm not saying anything against the Gorsets," Father said, "but when you go to a performance like that dinner tonight——" He skidded to a stop and looked alarmed. "Does that mean we owe *them* a dinner now?"

"No, of course not," Pat said, and he stopped vibrating.

"Like I always say," he said, "the best way to get along with neighbors is to have as little to do with——" He was interrupted by a scampering on the back porch and a knock at the door. Pat opened it, and there was Madge Gorset with a hunk of the uniced angel-food cake on a plate.

"I just thought I'd run this over for you, Pat," Madge said. "It's half of what was left, and Mr. Kraft was so nice about . . . Oh, hello, Mr. Kraft. I want to thank you for being so nice, buying all that stuff though there wasn't any obligation. You understood that, didn't you, but just the same——"

"Yes, yes," Father said, backing heavily out of his invaded kitchen. Madge seemed to fill it. "Don't mention it, Mrs. Gorset," he muttered, and fled to his easy chair, now an uneasy island, so it seemed, in a sudden seething sea of neighborliness.

# 10.  *Betrayal by Kin*

When a man in his middle fifties deliberately plunges himself into a strange new home life, he is either brave or
ignorant, I think. By this time in our new household—not
now so spanking new but still on trial—I was feeling that my
father had been less brave than ignorant. Bravery had little
to do with his original decision, for he had seen nothing to be
afraid of—but that was before he had collided with his out-
grown past, or stumbled over neighbors or religion, or had
to plot and scheme to keep some simple status quo from
foundering. And it seems to me it was at about this stage of
things that Father began losing his conviction that anything
that happened to him worked out well in the end. The thing
that makes me think so was his attitude toward the visit we
were to make to his sisters. He seemed to have a premonition
of bad luck.

The sisters were older than he—Lizzie sixteen years older
and Dean (short for Christina) eight years older—and they
had raised him and his two brothers after their parents died.
This experience had given these maidens a maternal out-

look on life and on my father. They knew all his faults and accepted them without forfeiting the privilege of reminding him about them; to him they were still his big sisters. He kept an eye on their welfare and saw them at regular intervals, and very little otherwise. They and their old-fashioned home reminded him too much of his youth, and he invariably began growing edgy the moment he arrived, until when he departed he was almost running for the door.

"Let's see," Pat said, consulting the kitchen calendar, "we're going to your sisters' house Saturday, Dad."

"Yump," he mumbled. "Guess there's no help for——" He broke off short. Apparently he had accidentally been thinking out loud.

"I'm interested in their house," she said. "I want to have a good look at it this time." She had been there only briefly before.

"House?" Father said. "That's a downstairs flat. And a mighty old-fashioned flat at that." The flat was in north St. Louis on Fair Avenue. Like most other flats on its block, it was of red brick, with white stone front steps. Inside, the polished woodwork was dark and the rooms smelled cool and antiseptic. I felt as Father did about the place, and I couldn't see why Pat had taken a fancy to it. "Liz and Dean never throw anything away," he said critically. While substantially true, this did seem an unjust slam, coming from Father. And for his sisters, throwing nothing away was a necessity. Their income was so small that they had to squeeze every penny. They squeezed them so well it was generally assumed in the neighborhood they were wealthy eccentrics, and they looked it when they sallied forth in rustling black dresses, carrying their long black gold-handled umbrellas, Lizzie tall and spare, and Dean short and wiry. Father had always considered it a blessing they could afford to be gentlewomen, unobliged to toil. He meant outside employment; in their own home they worked like crazy to make ends meet, but he didn't count that.

Before we left the house Saturday, Father spoke his mind about one thing. "Let's not stay too late," he said. "Sitting around there after dinner gives me the willies." As we left, Pat picked up a vase of roses picked from bushes in the yard. "You're bringing those?" Father said blankly.

"Why, yes," she said. "Don't they like flowers?"

"Well, Liz grows a few sweet Williams in the back yard," he admitted, but he looked at the bouquet glumly. "I think roses make her sneeze." It wouldn't have surprised me a bit. Lizzie was a walking clinic. However, she bore with her finicky insides with cheerfulness, and they provided her with unlimited small talk.

"I suppose they'll have chuck roast," Father said on the way over. He said it with a resigned air. "Chuck pot roast."

"No. Sauerbraten," Pat said, balancing the vase of roses on her lap as we short-cut a corner through a filling station and rocketed down a side street, exactly following the route Father always took to his sisters. Pat caught her breath. "They're fixing it because I like it."

"It's still chuck," Father grunted. "I just hope they don't forget my bread." His sisters always bought a family-sized loaf of bread at the grocery especially for Father, and he went through most of it during a meal there.

They met us at the door, wearing aprons but plainly having everything under control; they never seemed rushed when they had company arriving. "I picked you some flowers," Pat said, handing the roses over to Lizzie as the senior member of the household, "and I hope——"

"Ah-h-h—*choo-o-o-o*," said Lizzie, almost blowing the bouquet into the street. "Gesundheidt," Dean said, and took the roses off, out of inhaling distance. "Just like I said," Father said, and we all stepped inside.

In the front hall Pat stopped short. So did Father, right behind her. "What's the matter?" he said nervously, as if already reacting to the environment. She was fascinated, it turned out, by an old music box that worked with metal disks. It was one Father had got so tired of seeing in the parlor, he had tried to scuttle it by getting his sisters a modern radio-phonograph, but the old one had moved only as far as the hall. Lizzie set it to tinkling for Pat, and Father marched off, looking as if he was now sure this visit meant trouble.

"There's one thing about coming here for dinner," Ted said privately to me. "You don't have to sit around wondering when you're going to eat." This was so true that our aunts' home almost took on the air of a short-order house when we arrived. We were hardly inside before they began serving the food. Dean already had the sauerbraten rushed to the table by the time Lizzie turned off the music box, and we could hear Father in the dining room sharpening the carving knife and complaining about the illumination. The dining-room fixture had places for four light bulbs in a frosted-glass bowl; Lizzie, who took charge of all engineering details in running the house, standardized on twenty-five-watt bulbs throughout and then unscrewed two of the four in the dining-room bowl except when Father came to dine. Even with all four on the light seemed feeble.

"Downstairs flats are always a little dark, Ed," Father's sisters told him. "If you want light," Dean added, "you got to climb stairs." Lizzie nodded and added, "Light fades things too." Father shook himself impatiently and began to carve by feel. We passed around a plate of potato pancakes, skipping Father, who had his bread, and then a bowl of string beans that had been cooking all day. Also a dish of onions the aunts had pickled. If you liked German cooking, eating there was fine, but for Father it was an ordeal. It suddenly occurred to me that this may have been a big factor in his hastily asking Pat and me to come live with him. His sisters were just as hell-bent on doing their duty by him as he was by them, and it seemed likely he had learned they were perhaps planning to sacrifice themselves by moving in with him, lock, stock, and barrel. It would have been a fate worse than ulcers to Father.

As soon as dinner was over he went off to the parlor to read the newspapers. He was full of bread and water and

not a great deal else. There was iced tea, but he hadn't
touched it because there wasn't any lemon in it or any ice.
"Ach, the ice is all," Lizzie had said, peering into the pitcher.
"Maybe I should chip a little more, Liz?" Dean had said,
preparing for debate. They settled all questions by conference.

"Never *mind*," Father exclaimed. He glanced uneasily toward Pat. "I don't know why you won't let me buy you an
electric refrigerator," he shouted at his sisters. "Then you'd
have plenty of ice."

"We don't have any use for so much ice, Ed," Lizzie said.
"And," said Dean, "those things use too much good electricity." Father looked mortified, but he knew his kinfolk and
he didn't persist. He declined a helping of Lizzie's homemade
coffeecake and took himself off to the parlor. The coffeecake
was of bread dough and not nearly sweet enough for him.
His sisters were wonders at economizing, and during each
Christmas season they turned out a fruitcake that was egg-
less, butterless, and almost sugarless. Father said it was also
almost fruitless, the only pun I ever knew him to make, if
it was a pun.

"Well," he said when the rest of the party joined him in
the parlor shortly, "we'd better think about leaving. Don't
want to keep Liz up."

"You just got here, Ed," Lizzie said calmly, and rattled off
something to him in German. He looked utterly blank. "Two
years we spent good money to teach him German," she said
to Pat, "and he don't know nothing. All wasted." She spoke
impersonally and without rancor, as if Father was part of the
décor.

"What did you say in German?" Pat asked.

"I told him to stop the foot wiggle," Lizzie said. When he
was sitting, Father's feet were always going, and Ted and I
had inherited it, as if we all had to crank thoughts up from
the bottom. When Lizzie spoke, all our feet stopped for the
time being. "It wears out the socks," she said to Pat. Pat had
noticed holes in our socks, though she hadn't suspected the

wiggling. She had even darned a few of the holes. "So—*that's* it," she said.

Father snorted. "Nothing of the kind. Besides, I don't wiggle my feet," he said, resuming reading his paper and rotating his right foot like a pinwheel.

Lizzie and Pat looked at each other. "And I hate darning," Pat said. Father's foot went more wildly. "You're doing it again, Ed," Lizzie said. He flapped his foot on the floor and stood up. "Time to go," he said loudly. "Thanks for the meal and all——"

"Ed," Lizzie said, "Dean and I were cleaning out some things in the basement last week."

"Good," Father said of this seemingly irrelevant remark. "It's time you threw away some of the junk down there."

"Have you got an exercising thing at home?" Lizzie inquired. Father stared at her.

"A what?" he said after a moment.

"Something to take exercises with. Like at Turnvereins."

Father looked pained. "I don't need silly stuff like that. I've got a lot better things to do with my money."

Dean cackled. "This one cost plenty too. About fifty dollars."

"Fifty-two," Lizzie said. "Remember? Ed threw the bill in the stove, but we found it."

"What are you two talking about?" Father said testily.

For answer, his sisters led the way back to the kitchen and so down to the dark and high-ceilinged basement, divided down the middle by a lattice of boards segregating owners from tenants. The sisters' side had a laundry section in front, and ranged down the divider wall were storage units. They had been excavating one of them, and from it they now hauled a wooden crate about the size of an apple box. They set it on an old kitchen table, and in the murky light from a high window we could read on the crate front in red and black stencil: LITTLE DANDY MUSCLE BUILDER.

"What about it?" Father said, showing no desire to look farther.

"It's yours, Ed," his sisters said together.

He shook his head hard. "Pete or Al may have squandered their money on something like this," he said, referring to his brothers, "but not me. No siree, I had better sense even then——" He paused as Lizzie turned the crate around, looking for something.

"Make a light right here, Ed," she said, and frowning, he got a kitchen match from his vest pocket and struck it on the sole of one shoe. As it flared we could read an old shipping label on the crate. "To—Edward Otto Kraft, Esq.," it plainly said. Thirty-five years had not faded it much. Dean opened the box and pulled out the contraption. It had handles connected to springs which were connected to ropes connected to weights, and it was supposed to be mounted on a wall. The brackets for this were there, too, and so were the screws. Dean thrust the whole business at him. "You remember it now, Ed?" Father reluctantly fingered the hand grips. "You got it when you were sweet on Bertha Becker," Dean informed him.

But Lizzie shook her head. "That was after, Dean," she said. Dean was good at remembering details, but Lizzie was

a whiz. "Ed found out," she said, "that Adolph Kleinhaus sneaked over and took Bertha skating . . ." Father twitched and stretched the springs attached to the hand grips a bit.

"Ach, yes—now I remember," Dean said. "And Ed went running after that flirty Sophie Weingartner . . ." Lizzie shook her head again. "Before that there was the yellow-haired Oberfiest girl, their Bessie, the one who said he had such skinny muscles——"

With a jerk Father stretched the springs of the Little Dandy somewhat farther than he perhaps intended. The connecting ropes snapped and whipped through the air. Pat, Ted, and I, who had been listening with fascination to the historical details, ducked as the ropes lashed back. So did Father, and then he rammed the broken thing into its crate again with a force that proved his muscles were no longer skinny. Without a word he grabbed hold of the crate and lugged it upstairs, where he made a non-stop trip straight out to his car, picking up his hat on the way. He stowed the crate in his car trunk, locked the lid, and stood waiting, twitching his feet.

"Oh," Pat said when we had all traipsed back up, "well, I guess we have to go, Aunt Lizzie and Dean. I've had a perfectly lovely time."

"Me too," I said. "Very educational."

"Let us know next time you're going to clean some more things out of the basement," Ted said.

Father was silent in a stern sort of way on the trip home, as if he was daring somebody to say something. Nobody did, at least to him, and finally he spoke. "I think Liz and Dean are beginning to show their age," he said rather abruptly as he raced a Delmar streetcar to a corner. None of us said anything. His sisters had looked pretty lively to us. "They ought to take things easier," he said. "Dammit, I'm just going to go ahead and get them that electric refrigerator. If it runs up their electric bill, I'll pay the difference."

I thought it pretty noble of him, considering everything.

However, the sisters raised such loud objections to his spending the money that he had to fool them by buying a new refrigerator himself and telling them they might just as well take his old one because the dealer wouldn't allow him hardly anything. They refused to accept anything extra for their electric bill, though, and instead studied to see what they could do for him in return for the refrigerator. They hit upon sock darning, which suited Pat just fine. For Father it turned out to be a mixed blessing; he had to set up a weekly sock drop and pickup at his sisters' house each Wednesday, and when he got home on Wednesday evening after that he was ten minutes behind schedule and looked punchy, as if he had worked out too hard on the muscle-builder machine. Incidentally, we never heard any more about it from him or about any of the flip north St. Louis girls of his skinny, spendthrift salad days.

# 11. *Sarah and the Saints*

My father was an impatient man, I hardly need say at this point, always in a fever to hurry fate along as if he was anxious to hear even bad news quickly. On top of this he was one of the most prejudiced men I ever met, which influenced his haste in subtle ways. He held opinions on everything, either for or against, no middle ground and no nonsense about keeping an open mind. The open mind, he believed, was the sloppy mind. Still, this is not to say he never changed an opinion. Such a thing occurred at this point in our life with him, right on the heels of the bumpy visit to his sisters, and it put him in a novel and embarrassing position he had never before suffered in his own home. The thing that tripped him was a saint; several saints in fact.

What began it was Katy's decision to stop being a maid of all work and to become a capitalist. She announced she was opening a barbecue stand, so Pat wished her luck, contributed some spare kitchen equipment to the enterprise, and then looked around for another helping hand. This turned out to be Sarah Plim. Prior to her arrival there had never been a saint in Father's home. Sarah was a large, moist, florid woman of thirty-five or so who was intense about everything she did, from peeling a potato to saving her soul, and she never laughed. A few days after she started working for us, Father overheard her in the midst of a private conversation when he happened to go down to the basement.

Sarah was down there hanging up some dish towels she had just washed out. She was always washing something. Because of the dish towels Father could see only the top of her head, but he could hear her plainly enough. She was talking to some other woman in an easy, chatty sort of way, someone she called Saint Gertrude. Father couldn't see the top of Saint Gertrude's head so he stooped and looked hard underneath the dish towels for her legs, but all he saw were Sarah's legs, shaped like tenpins. He was not a connoisseur or even much of a fancier of legs; his only purpose in looking was to locate Sarah's friend, and he disapproved of eavesdropping so he abruptly cleared his throat. The conversation paused. "Excuse me, Saint Gertrude," Sarah said behind the dish towels, and came out.

"I didn't mean to interrupt your talk," Father said. "I— uh . . ." He waited, thinking the friend might take the hint and step out to say hello. He was generally a sociable man and got on well with women who treasured the reassurance of a comfortably masculine man who was handsome to boot.

"Oh, that's all right," Sarah said earnestly. "Saint Gertrude understands it's during working hours."

"Did you say . . . *Saint* Gertrude?" Father asked after a moment.

Sarah nodded affably. "I was just asking if she'd mind keeping the mice away when I'm down here hanging up, if there's any mice." Father did not reply immediately. "I'm scared to death of mice, Mr. Kraft," Sarah explained, "and you know how basements are, and Saint Gertrude is invoked for mice. And even though she does have a lot more important things, purgatory and all . . ." Father began backing toward the stairs, keeping his eyes on Sarah. "Is anything the matter, Mr. Kraft?" she asked. He shook his head very slightly. "Ah—your neck's stiff," she declared. "Well, Saint Ursicinus is the one to——"

"Nothing's the matter," Father said, making it to the stairs and bounding up them. "Nothing, nothing," he shouted back, and sped off for my wife, to whom he gave a rapid account of what was going on in the basement. "I thought at first it was some*body*, and then I thought she'd been talking to herself," he said, "and the whole time she was talking to some saint. *A saint.*"

"Yes," Pat said. "Sarah's quite devout."

"You've heard her too?" Father exclaimed.

"Strictly speaking, I suppose she's praying," my wife said, "but she feels so close to the saints, it sounds like ordinary conversation."

"Not ordinary," Father muttered. "I guess you wouldn't know about a Saint Ursicinus, would you? Seems to be good for stiff necks." He went off looking troubled. The only saints he was used to hearing mentioned were a few whose names had been taken by Episcopal churches, such as Saint Philip and Saint Michael, and it had never occurred to him to pray to them, any more than he would have prayed to a steeple. I don't know that he prayed at all, but if he did, it would have been straight up to God and in stylized terms. Sarah's vernacular approach was unsettling to him, and he soon discovered he was apt to run into it at any moment and in any corner of his house. He knew practically nothing about any religion but the Episcopalian and didn't want to. Though several of his close friends were good Roman Catholics, they didn't pray out loud, and he felt so comfortable around them he frequently forgot about their religion for hours at a time. Around Sarah he couldn't forget for five minutes.

"Is your neck better, Mr. Kraft?" she asked him next time she saw him.

"What's the matter with your neck?" I said. It looked all right to me except that it was suddenly getting red.

"Nothing's the matter with my neck," he said, addressing

both of us. "Thanks, though," he added rather fumblingly to Sarah.

"Don't thank me, thank Saint Ursicinus," she said, and started running the vacuum cleaner and shoving furniture around. She was strong and shoved things easily.

"Who's he?" I yelled at Father over the howl of the cleaner. He looked annoyed. "How do I know?" he shouted back. "One of her saints, that's all. The stiff-neck saint."

"Seems to me you know a good deal," I said when we had gone to the back porch, away from the uproar. I looked him over. "*Was* your neck stiff?"

He ran his hand uneasily over the back of his neck. "I don't know. A little, I suppose. I probably slept crooked the night before." He closed the conversation by striding off to dust his car, a job he always found so soothing that he drove the cleanest automobile in University City.

I hunted up Ted, who was upstairs studying. "Dad's mixed up with a saint," I said. "Heard anything?"

"Oho," Ted said. "One of Sarah's." He consulted a note on his desk. "Saint Vincent de Paul?"

"No. But what about this one?"

"We're calling him in—well, Sarah is—for consultation. He's a saint appealed to for finding lost articles, and I seem to have lost my left slipper." He was wearing the right one, I saw. "Have you heard her?" he asked. I hadn't. "It's interesting," he said. "It's as if she was talking to a friend. Respectful and all, but not like praying. It's a little spooky."

"I haven't any favors to request," I said, "but I'd like——"

"If you two are talking about Sarah," my wife said, coming upon us suddenly, "just remember she has strong feelings about this. I don't want you to do anything that'd bother her. Good help's scarce."

"She's the last person I'd think of bothering," I said. "I'm sincerely interested. I'd like to know more about this." However, I didn't see how to strike up a conversation with Sarah on the subject. Asking what she'd heard from the saints lately seemed in questionable taste and possibly sacrilegious. The

best thing would be to ask for help in some affliction, I supposed, and I was obviously as healthy as a horse. But a day or
two later I picked up another side light vicariously. Father,
it came out, was also now missing something—several pairs of
fancy summer socks he had impulsively bought while tearing
through Famous-Barr on some other errand and which he
had not yet squeezed room for in the sock drawer of his
mahogany bureau.

"As long as Saint Vincent is hunting for my slipper," Ted
said, "maybe he could keep an eye out for your socks."

Father frowned. "Don't talk like that. It doesn't sound——"
He skidded. "What's that about Saint Somebody and your
slipper?"

"Saint Vincent de Paul. Sarah says he's invoked in
searches, and my left slipper's gone." He returned Father's
gaze. "Well, she suggested it."

"Don't go encouraging her," Father said sharply. "They're
her saints, not ours."

When Sarah heard about the lost socks, however, her natural reaction asserted itself. "Dad doesn't know it yet," Ted
advised me, "but Saint Anthony's looking for his socks."

"He's new, isn't he?" I asked, and Ted said he was. "Seems
wasteful," I said. "There was already Saint Vincent, and
now——"

"Well, after all, *no*body's found my slipper yet." He was
still wearing the other and was temporarily using a shower
clog on his left foot, an arrangement that gave his tread upstairs an eerie, delayed clumping and bothered Father, feeling as he did that the house was full of saints. It also had
another effect: as he sat studying for final exams at his desk,
Ted's feet wiggled and once in a while the clog dropped off.
Each time it did, Father, Pat, and I, sitting in the living
room below, jumped, and Father's and my feet wiggled
furiously. This was hardest on Pat, who lacked the emotional
release of the wiggle, and she happened to say something
about it one morning to Sarah, who was playing the piano.
She often played a few bars by ear while dusting the keys.

Sarah took the wiggling in single-tracked stride. "When you're not sure who to go to, Saint Joseph is very helpful," she said. "But on the other hand, maybe I'd better ask around." Pat thought she heard Sarah mentioning it to Saint Joseph anyway later that day while shoving furniture. She felt awkward about the turn the chat had taken and would have been relieved if Sarah had forgotten to follow it up. She didn't forget, and it turned out that wiggling was far from uncommon as a cause of supplication to the saints.

Whoever Sarah asked—probably one of the dozens of nuns she knew—especially urged Saint Bartholomew as helpful in nervous diseases and twitchings. "Well, that certainly hits the nail on the head," my wife said. "Describes it so well, that is." She hesitated, not wanting to take the initiative, but feeling that as long as Sarah had gone to the trouble, it would be discourteous to her not to invite Saint Bartholomew to see what he could do.

"But also," Sarah continued, "there's Saint Cornelius. He's called in for epilepsy too."

Pat moistened her lips. "That's pretty . . . strong——"

"*And* there's Saint Claude," Sarah concluded.

"Another one?" Pat cried.

"Saint Claude is also invoked for bad luck," Sarah said, and Pat caught a faint twinge of debate in her tone. "Well," she said quickly, "a thing like that's bound to keep him busy. On the whole, Saint Bartholomew seems more of a specialist, if that's the word."

The upshot of this discussion was a formal request to Saint Bartholomew, if you could call Sarah's approach formal, to intercede in our foot wiggling. I hope it did some good. Indeed, who can say it did not? Father's, Ted's, and my feet wiggled on, but the wiggling grew no worse—and this in the face of a terrible nervousness now brewing within Father.

He was being nervous about Ted's final exams. Ted's grades for the year had been good, but Father feared the worse because he was desperately anxious to become the father of a doctor. He was frequently torn between despair over having to wait seven more long years for this blessing and panic lest Ted should study too fast and get washed out, as had the son of a chemist in Father's office. Ted slightly knew the chemist's son from school meetings and had stated to Father that the poor lad was a meathead, born to fizzle, but Father was not lulled by this. He foresaw Ted fizzling, too, for he thought the chemist a very bright fellow and assumed his son must be brilliant. About his own get, Father had no illusions.

As the tension mounted daily, it was inevitable Sarah would figure in this made-to-order situation, and sure enough —presently it came out that Ted was being prayed for to Saint Catherine of Alexandria. Sarah mentioned it to Pat, in very much the same manner she had mentioned a few moments before that she had started the refrigerator defrosting. When Pat asked who Saint Catherine was, Sarah answered that she was a patroness of students. In view of this powerful influence, it seems surprising that later that very morning a bedbug was found in Ted's bed, souvenir of a free clinic the medical students had just toured.

The discovery of the bedbug so exercised both Pat and

Sarah, they spent the rest of the day in a frenzied house-cleaning of the bedroom and were still suspicious when they had finished, so that after we got home, Father, Ted, and I found ourselves absently scratching, and Sarah seemed to think she should say something to Ted in Saint Catherine's defense. It was the first time he knew of Saint Catherine's interest in him, or of Saint Catherine for that matter, and he was not very gracious about it. His bed was reeking of disinfectant, and he acted grumpy about the sex of his patroness, as if comparing her with the dean of men at the university, to her disadvantage.

Though not admitting that Saint Catherine had been remiss about the bedbug, Sarah took out spiritual insurance, so to speak; she began making a novena, after carefully considering which of the saints she still had in reserve would be most likely to scoot my brother through his examinations. Meanwhile, de-bedbugging the bedroom had had a useful corollary effect—both Ted's left slipper and Father's new socks were recovered, found jammed behind furniture Sarah had shoved at one time or another. She gave Saints Vincent de Paul and Anthony credit for the find, and Father was short with Ted when he laughed at this, though he had not laughed in front of Sarah.

By the end of the next ten days my brother had taken all his finals and, as he had patiently kept predicting, passed. "The saints be praised," he said, and Father glanced at him from under his eyebrows.

"I think now," Father said guardedly, "it would be a very nice thing if you said something to Sarah."

"Said something?" Ted repeated.

Father jammed his hands into his pants pockets and yanked them out again. "If you spoke to her," he said.

Ted gave him an obtuse look he had developed for the purpose, and exasperation reddened Father's neck and jowls. "You might at least thank her, dammit," he roared, and seemed immediately to regret his worldly tone. "After all, you

can't tell about those things," he muttered. "You passed, didn't you?"

With some dignity my brother produced a rumpled piece of note paper from his shirt pocket. "While I was crossing the quadrangle to pick up my grades," he said, "I stopped at the library and looked up a dictionary of the saints." He consulted his note paper. "Would you care to know who all this Saint Catherine patronizes besides us stoodents? Saddlers, ropemakers, and spinsters—that's who."

"Well, what of it?" Father said.

"All right," Ted said. "That isn't all. That novena Sarah made to help me along was to a Saint Jude. Looked him up too." Father waited, fidgeting. "'Saint Jude,'" Ted read. "'Invoked when the situation is desperate.'" He looked coldly at Father, who nodded without a hint of criticism; he always did approve of strong measures, promptly taken. "Well, you passed," he said again, "remember that."

When it became plain that Ted was not going to say anything at all to Sarah, Father a little self-consciously pressed a five-dollar bill on her. "For your church," he insisted when she at first refused. In all his life before he had never given the Roman Catholic Church a dime, and it took Easter Sunday to get five dollars out of him for the Episcopal Church. Sarah accepted the money on that basis and told him it would be as bread cast upon the waters. "I've been thinking that next time I'll pray to Saint Expedite for you, Mr. Kraft," she said, taking it for granted that Father would be needing help again.

"Expedite?" Father said. "There's actually a Saint *Expedite*?"

"Saint Expedite," Sarah repeated, savoring the name while she regarded Father with moistly intense approval. Then she proved how well she had sized him up. "Saint Expedite," she said, "is for when you're usually in kind of a rush."

# 12. *Happy Birthday, Father*

If Father could have stopped having birthdays and kept on getting birthday presents it would have been an ideal arrangement. Ted and I had never sympathized with his skittishness about aging, but at least we knew about it; Pat had never run into such an attitude, and she simply didn't believe it. This was the situation when Father's first birthday in his remodeled household approached, shortly after Ted's final examinations.

"How many candles do I put on Dad's cake?" Pat asked me. He never stated how old he was. I had ferreted it out for myself years before by arithmetic after he made the error of saying he had been twenty-one years old when a certain photograph was taken. He did not notice until too late that the photograph was dated.

"No candles," I told my wife, "if you expect him to digest this cake. Fifty-four if you feel reckless. Are you planning much of a party?"

"Well, I think we ought to do something nice," she said. "It's personal attention. And Sarah dotes on parties and she's anxious to do something for Dad because of that money he gave her for the church."

I felt that with Sarah and her influence on Father's side his birthday should be better than usual. However, when Pat asked him what kind of birthday cake he'd like, she got a big setback. "I don't think he even wants a birthday cake," she cried at me. "He said not to make a big fuss. Do you suppose he's sick or something?"

I didn't think he was sick. "As a matter of fact," I said, "he's always taken the view he's immortal. He's never made a will, for instance."

"But it's just a birthday cake. And anyway, I've——"

"There is more here than meets the eye," I told her. "Father is a paradox. He wants to be the old man of the tribe here at home, and at the same time he wants to be a perpetual young fellow."

"Well," she said, "I've already——"

"In fact, as the years go by," I said, "you can guess his age pretty closely by noticing who he calls young fellows. They're always men around his own age. Those about ten years younger he calls boys. He knows quite a few forty-year-old boys. So you see how he feels about birthday parties. Presents are fine, but parties——"

"I do wish you'd listen a minute," she said. "I've already made plans for a party and I can't call it off now. It's to be kind of a surprise."

"You haven't invited any guests?"

She nodded brightly. "His sisters."

"Well," I said, "after that surprise he won't want any more of your surprises for the rest of the year." His two sisters were very much aware of birthdays and other vital statistics in the family. They seemed to get a lot out of keeping up on such things, frequently refreshing their information by visiting Frieden's Cemetery, an old north-side German burying ground where most of their late friends and relations lay. The only times Father went near the place between funerals was when he took Lizzie and Dean there on a joy ride.

I agreed to pick his sisters up at their flat after I left my office Friday evening, Father's birthday, and then I asked if Pat had anything in mind for a birthday present. "He's tough to buy for," I said. "Whatever you pick, he's either already got it or he wouldn't have it. If you want my advice, let's give him whisky. He can't complain about the color or pattern."

She vetoed the whisky. "I'll think of something nice," she said. "It can be from all three of us." This relieved Ted and me of doing anything, for which we were truly thankful. In years of gift buying for Father we had seldom pleased him. It was curious that his enthusiasm for receiving presents continued so high in view of our punk record, but it did. Each time he opened one of our gifts his eyes snapped with anticipation as if this one was going to ring the bell, and when it flopped he was melancholy but not surprised. This time he seemed to suspect something different was afoot, probably because he was used to being plied with sly questions to find out what he wanted. But as his birthday approached, neither Pat, Ted, nor I quizzed him, and it began to show in his behavior; he felt hurt by the seeming indifference and took refuge in silent dignity. "Maybe we ought to tell him Pat's taking the rap this year," Ted said, but I felt it might spoil the surprise. She hadn't bought a present yet but she had the calm complacency of ignorance that she could find something just right, and at the last minute if she had to.

By Friday evening Father was a thoroughly disillusioned man. Evidently he had kept a spark of hope that none of us was really taking seriously his indifference toward celebrating his birthday, but when he got home from work the spark went out completely. Pat had the birthday cake hidden, and nothing seemed much different than usual except that I wasn't home yet. Pat said I was picking something up for her, and she fixed Father an old-fashioned. He took it off glumly and dumped himself into his easy chair. Ted came downstairs and spoke to him and felt for a moment that Father might dash his old-fashioned at him, he looked so aggrieved.

When his sisters and I arrived, however, things picked up. I escorted them up the front walk feeling as if I were squiring a pair of duchesses, for they were in their black silks with white lace dickies at the throats and flourishing their gold-handled umbrellas. The shock of seeing his sisters descending on him without warning yanked Father's mind off his moodiness, and he sprang out of his chair as we entered the front door, flung open by Pat, who had been listening from the kitchen for our coming.

"What's the matter?" Father cried hoarsely, apparently thinking nothing but a death in the family could account for the abrupt visitation.

Lizzie planted a kiss squarely on his forehead and Dean popped him on the chin. "Happy birthday, Ed," they cried as one woman.

"Well, well," Father said. "Well, well, well." Taking heart, he went down to the wine cellar and fetched up a bottle of a sort of sherry type he had made a few years before and considered the best he ever produced. He poured glasses all around, and after one for politeness' sake Pat, Ted, and I withdrew to the kitchen and left Father and his sisters toasting each other.

"Enjoy yourself while you can, Ed," I heard Lizzie say. "At your age Papa was dead five years already." This was followed by an impressive silence of several seconds. I was impressed, too, reflecting that in his tinted photograph in the sisters' parlor their papa looked about eighty. I began to feel that our father was remarkably well preserved, all things considered.

"To Uncle Heinrich," Dean said, proposing another toast. He was really their and Father's great-uncle. "Ach, Uncle Heinrich," Lizzie said gloomily. "His birthday is next August nineteenth. A hundred and twenty-four years old." Pat, happening to tune in on this, almost dropped the birthday cake.

"She means he'd be a hundred and twenty-four if he were alive," I told her. "He's been dead about sixty years."

"Liz and I were out to see about Fritz and Oscar last Sunday, Ed," we heard Dean say. Father grunted. "Their lot's in terrible shape," she said.

"Who're Fritz and Oscar?" Pat asked me in the kitchen. "Real-estate people?" I told her they were second cousins.

"Weeds all over Oscar's grave," Lizzie said, "and Fritz's headstone is crooked."

Pat gave me a wild look. "Birthdays always do this to Dad's sisters," I said. "Of course, you didn't know that when you invited them."

But talking about the dead always had an uplifting effect on Father's sisters, as I had noticed before. They brightened up as they went along. By the time dinner was on the table they were tittering and making little jokes as Father escorted them in, looking as if he had been having a cozy chat with the undertaker.

Knowing Lizzie's dietary limitations, Pat had chopped spinach and a baked potato for her in place of the broccoli and Yorkshire pudding she served the rest of us, and Father dutifully sawed her off the best outside slice of roast beef.

When Pat brought the birthday cake to the table she explained that instead of candles it had an inscription. Sarah Plim had lovingly done it herself in pink icing on white. She had put "Happy Birthday to Mister Kraft," and then, having space left over, she had worked in a few stars and a "St. Exp." at the very bottom. It was a reference to the Saint Expedite she was expecting to appeal to for Father, but it looked a little as if the saint had sent Father the cake personally, signing it like a letter. Father whacked his knife right through the "St. Exp." before his sisters could get a good look. They were members of the Evangelical Church and would have been dismayed if they had known what the letters on their slices stood for. But as it was they thought they were eating pink scallops, and cake was not yet off Lizzie's diet list.

The subject of Father's birthday present suddenly occurred to me as we were finishing. Ever since Ted and I had
gladly dumped it on Pat, neither of us had thought much
about it. Now I wondered if she could possibly have forgotten to get him something, and when the meal ended I
managed to get her aside and ask. Ted, too, had been wondering. "Of course I didn't forget," she said. "I got him a
perfectly lovely present. Very useful, too, and it's something
he doesn't have."

"You're a genius," Ted said. "What is it, a passkey to the
mint?"

"It's a dressing gown," she said with a superior smile. "A
gorgeous silk dressing gown *and* a pair of slippers to match."
Ted and I just looked at each other. "Well?" Pat said. "Isn't
that something he doesn't have?"

"It sure is," I said. It had never occurred to me to tell her
how Father felt about dressing gowns and slippers. He
wouldn't even use a bathrobe, and as to slippers—"I don't
want to get into the habit of changing to slippers when I
come home," he would explain distinctly to anyone who mentioned it, "because there might be an evening when I'd
have to keep my shoes on, see?" Ted and I, at least, saw, and
perhaps more clearly than Father thought. He was refusing
to pamper himself; young fellows should not get soft.

Pat hauled the birthday presents out of the pantry. They
made quite a showing, all gift-wrapped, almost like a Christmas. "He'll love us," Ted said, "till he gets them open." We
filed into the living room, Greeks bearing gifts.

Father was already looking restive, apparently calculating
how soon he could decently get his sisters moving homeward,
and the appearance of presents took him by surprise. He
gazed eagerly at the promising-looking suit box that held the
dressing gown and at the interesting slipper box, and he
nearly drooled. His eyes shifted to the three of us with a fond
look of forgiveness, and he began clawing off gift wrappings
on the slipper box after weighing it in his hand and shaking
it a few times. I think he supposed it was a belt, since it was

too heavy for handkerchiefs and too light for a cigar humidor. When he had got to the box itself he peered at the label on the lid. "Slippers," he said. "It says slippers. Ho, ho." He opened the box and the laugh died in his throat. "Good Lord," he said, "it *is* slippers."

"Well, let's have a look, Ed," Lizzie said. "Take them out." He held them up in a numb way. They were of red leather with black patent-leather trim. "Why, they're nice enough to take a walk in," Lizzie said, and Father made a gurgling sound.

"Maybe you'd better try them for size, Dad," Pat said. "I had to guess."

He slowly undid the laces of his right shoe, pulled it off, and rammed his foot into a slipper. He wrestled up from his easy chair and, clasping his gift boxes to his bosom, walked tenderly across the room and back. "I don't know," he mumbled. "It doesn't feel exactly——"

"You're wearing the left slipper on your right foot, Ed," Dean said, looking keenly at his feet. Blinking, Father switched slippers. "How does it feel now?" Dean demanded. "Fine," Father said hopelessly. "Just fine."

He returned to his chair and started to get back into his shoe. "Try the other one, too, Ed," Lizzie said. "Maybe your feet are different sizes."

"They're the same size," Father said testily, but he put the other slipper on. They gave him a luxurious English air from the ankles down. Suddenly he remembered the other package and brightened as he began opening it. I think he anticipated a raincoat, though he should have realized we would have been out of our minds to buy him one; he already had three. However, the box was about the right weight to be holding a raincoat, and when he shook it now and then as he tore off ribbon and wrapping, it sounded a little like a raincoat. There was no clue on the lid of this box, so he didn't get the full force of the dressing gown until he had the lid off. And even then he didn't know what it was at first. He lifted it slowly out of the box and it unfurled before his bewildered eyes. It was maroon and black, with a tasseled sash around the middle and frog fasteners.

"That's a right pretty kimono," Dean said, and Father almost dropped it.

"Dressing gown," Pat said quickly. "And I do hope it's the right size." The doomed man rose to his slippered feet and slowly climbed into his dressing gown. I held it for him and Ted tied the sash in a tasteful square knot. Father stood like a statue; ordinarily he didn't care for any help with his clothes.

"Now walk, Ed," Lizzie said, and he stalked down the length of the room and back, the gown billowing about his legs, the slippers flapping softly on the thick rug. He looked like a different man.

"How do you think it fits in the shoulders, Aunt Lizzie?" Pat asked.

Lizzie halted Father and ran her hand over the shoulders while he stood fidgeting. "There's kind of a lump here," she murmured. "See if you can feel it, Pat."

Pat tried. "I can feel . . . something," she said.

"I don't know if it's the fit or if it's Ed," Lizzie said. "Ed, have you got lumps——"

"That's my shirt," Father snarled, wrenching free and giving his shirt sleeve a yank. For a few moments he stood still, apparently trying to hit on a way of shucking off his birthday presents without appearing thankless, and then a way came to him. "Well," he said to his sisters, "we don't want to keep you up too late. If you're ready to go——" He untied the sash of his gown.

"I'm going to take Aunt Liz and Dean home, Dad," I said without thinking. "My car's out front."

"Yes, you stay comfortable, Ed," Lizzie said. "You look right snug," Dean added. Father slowly retied the sash, and I got my aunts' hats and umbrellas.

"I think I'll come too," Ted said when we were ready to leave. Gowned and slippered, Father stood at the front door with Pat while Ted and I armed our aunts down the porch steps. They turned to wave good-by when we reached the sidewalk, but a neighbor was passing by and Father disappeared suddenly behind my wife. Only one hand remained in sight, rising out of a maroon sleeve and black satin cuff, dismally waving good-by over Pat's shoulder.

"I think it's nice of you to make your father so comfortable," our aunt Lizzie said on the way home. "At his age a man should take things mighty easy."

It was a remark we did not forward to Father. "Anyway, he's had enough birthday today to last him a spell," I said to Ted on the way home, and Ted said he thought Father had better skip the next seven or eight, until he caught up with the aging he had done today.

# 13. *Water, Water, Everywhere*

Father's prestige in his campaign for a household that should orbit admiringly around him seemed at a record low now that his birthday had come, mauled him, and gone, but still another blow was just around the corner. It never rains but it pours, as they say, and this time it was literally a cloudburst that descended on Father.

For the first few years after he had built his house the basement walls had leaked like screens each time it rained. He had gradually checked this by plugging up the leaky places with cement, and in recent years the basement had stayed dry enough to store things in. Father, who always needed room for storage, had an old wardrobe down there half filled with cardboard boxes of things. He offered Pat the other half of the wardrobe for dead storage, but she didn't trust basements. "I've never seen one that wasn't damp *sometimes*," she told him. "Are you sure the things you've got down there aren't mildewing right this minute?" Father scoffed at the thought. "Well, I think you ought to look to make sure," she said. "Would you like me to look?"

"No, no," Father said quickly. "They're just personal things —sentimental value," and he settled the question by hurrying down to the basement and having a look for himself. "All fine and dandy," he reported back. "Dry as toast down there."

Pat remained unconvinced, but she didn't bother Father's wardrobe storage, whatever it was. It took the river Des Peres to do that.

The river Des Peres wasn't much of a river. It wasn't even much of a creek except in rainy spells. In fact, it was a kind of stagnant nuisance meandering through county and city, and a project of enclosing it in a huge concrete pipe was then going on. The construction had just reached our neighborhood, and by strolling the half block down Trinity to Dartmouth, which skirted the river, we could see the latest section of the pipe in place, a pipe so big a man could walk through it, and also the excavation widening the river bed where the next section would go. We had been having a dry spell and the river was not flowing at all. Apparently the contractor felt he had led too upright a life for it to rain on him unexpectedly, for one Friday night he allowed a great pile of earth to remain like a dam across the dry river bed. And—wouldn't you know?—quite early that evening the rain began, very, very suddenly and hard.

"This'll do the lawn good," Father panted when he had raced the rain from the garage to the house when he got home. "But it doesn't have to *pour* so," he added. He seldom gave the weather a passing grade, but this rain was unusually hard, the drops bouncing up from street and rooftops to form layers of haze a foot deep, and we could hardly see the mailbox that stood at the curb in front, beside our driveway.

Father loped around the house checking windows and had a quick look at basement and attic. Nothing was leaking. But during dinner the rain grew even harder, and Father paused to hunt up candles in the buffet drawer. The electricity justified him by failing as soon as dinner was over, and for a while he strove to read the newspapers by candlelight.

He didn't have much luck, but it did not greatly matter because he could never sit still during a storm anyway. He kept jumping up to see the rain raining, and presently we heard him trumpeting from the front porch.

"Look at the street!" he cried when we hurried out. There was no street to look at. It had become a canal.

"Why aren't the sewers draining it off?" Pat cried.

"They will, they will," Father said. "I can see it going down already, I think."

Now this was terribly wishful thinking. There was that earthen dam across the river Des Peres; it had backed the storm water into a lake already dotted with houses in lower-lying areas north and west of us, and all the sewers were drowned. But we didn't know about this dam or the lake, and Father's faith in the University City sewer system was strong. "*Now* it'll go down," he said as the rain abruptly stopped. There was a constant sound of running water now, as it drained down the hill from Delmar Boulevard, about a quarter mile away.

"Can you tell how high it is now, Dad?" Pat asked him, for he could see in the dark like an owl. But just then the electricity came back on and a lamppost across the street lighted. It was standing in at least a foot of water. "And here it comes creeping up our driveway," Pat cried.

Father gave the water in the driveway a stern look. It had advanced twenty feet up the gentle slope. Then he brightened. "The concrete curbing will keep it where it belongs," he said.

At that moment something happened that had never happened before. In the light from the street lamp a canoe came floating toward us, gently paddled along Amherst Canal by a middle-aged neighbor. "Curious evening, what?" he said as he passed. Father looked stonily after him while he paddled on down Trinity. "That's a fool stunt," he said. "In five minutes the water'll be gone and he'll have to carry that thing back on his head."

"Don't be too sure," Ted murmured. "There's a foot of water on the sidewalk now, and our driveway keeps right on filling." I don't think Father heard him, for a little diversion was taking place beside the mailbox.

A Mr. Drury who lived across the street was standing there at the mailbox on one foot, his pants rolled up to his knees. He was on his way home and he was now eying that haven, across the stormy waters. Father knew him no better than he knew any neighbor, but he approved of him because he wore a coat when he mowed his front lawn. Now, on an impulse, he called out to Mr. Drury.

"Care to wait here while the water goes down?" he sang out, indicating the sanctuary of our porch. "Ten more minutes'll do it."

"Ten *minutes!*" Mr. Drury said. "Why, it's risen a good inch up my knees since I got here, Kraft."

Father disliked being called by his barefoot last name, and he didn't care a bit about having his judgment doubted. "Let him wade across, then," he muttered. "And he'll have a mighty wet pair of pants when he——" Father let it hang, his mouth open as he stared. The respectable Mr. Drury, having removed his shoes and balanced them on top of the mailbox, was now removing his pants. Then, holding shoes and pants on high, he struck out into deep water, steering for his front-porch steps. His polka-dot shorts, black and yellow, were a beacon as he stalked like a crane making for a lakeside nest, and this seemed particularly to offend Father. "Fancy underpants," he croaked.

He seemed about to apologize to Pat for the neighborhood, when she spoke for herself. "That's the most sensible thing I ever saw," she said. "And look—he's even going to go in by their basement door, so he won't track water through the house." The Drury basement door was on the side of their house, in our view.

Father remained disgruntled. "Just let him get out of sight," he muttered.

Mr. Drury did get out of sight but only for a few seconds. Then he came back into sight so suddenly that he seemed to have made a standing high jump up his basement area-way steps. He began sloshing madly for his front porch, yelling for his wife, and even Father's reserve was shaken loose. "Is anything the matter?" he roared nervously across the waves, and Mr. Drury shot him a wild look over his shoulder.

"Matter?" he bawled. "My whole goddam basement's flooded, that's what's the matter. You better go look . . ." Father didn't wait to hear the rest. He was already galloping into the house with the rest of us hot on his trail while Mr. Drury was still talking. We thundered down the basement stairs, and ahead of us Father began gibbering with relief.

"See? See?" he cried. "Only a little water here. Hardly any. Just these little pools around the drains." At the moment it didn't strike him or the rest of us that it was peculiar the drains weren't draining. They were, as a matter of fact, back-ing up. Father glanced swiftly around. "And there's a little seeping in under the door. . . ." He looked harder. We all looked. "You know," Pat said in a puzzled way, "that *looks* something like water through the window part of the door. Isn't that funny?"

Ted and I started over to see about it, when suddenly the door creaked heavily and seemed to bulge. "Look out!" Fa-ther shouted. "It *is* water!" We all sprang for the stairs as the door burst open like a bomb and about five hundred gallons of water dumped in from the areaway. Immediately a torrent began tumbling in from outside as it cascaded down the area-way steps, and in an astonishingly short while the basement floor was under three feet of water.

Backed up on the stairs, watching the current swirling by, we estimated the probable damages each in our own way. "If it goes over the tool bench," Ted said to me, "we're ruined men." He and I stood to lose possibly fifty dollars' worth of planes, chisels, drills, and so on, or at least have them get awfully rusty.

Pat thought of the cleaning that was coming. "This muddy, muddy water," she moaned. "I'll have to take a shovel to this basement."

Father was eying the furnace. "My good oil burner," he muttered. "Ruined, I suppose." He supposed rightly; the flooded parts had to be replaced, and the replacements cost $200. But that was just money. Father was in for a greater loss, and it now began to happen.

As we stood on the basement stairs, the old wardrobe where Father had stored what he called things of sentimental value was around the corner of the enclosed staircase, where we could not see it. But as the water rose, the wardrobe's thin doors bulged and came open, the cardboard storage boxes floated out, and carried on the current, they began to pass in review before us, round and round the basement.

I guess Father recognized them, even as damp and soggy as they now were. He didn't say so, though, and the rest of us had no idea what the boxes held. Anyway, they were too far away to reach until Ted thought of the broom. He fished in a little box with it and the limp cardboard fell apart in his hands. He held up the small metal object the box had contained and he, Pat, and I looked blankly at it. It looked like a tiny teakettle with a wick in its spout and a hook for a handle. "Well, *I've* never seen this thing before," Ted said at last, "and I've been all *over* this basement." He looked at Father. "It must have come out of your wardrobe."

"Yes, yes," Father said, flushing. He reached for the little teakettle.

"But what *is* it, Dad?" Pat asked.

"A miner's lamp," he said shortly.

"I didn't know you were ever a miner," Ted said. "Why doesn't somebody tell me these——"

"I *wasn't*," Father shouted. We waited. "I bought it a long time ago," he said reluctantly. "I thought it would be handy at night."

"You went around with this torch on your head?" Ted cried. "What did people say?"

"Dammit," Father said, "I kept chickens. I wanted it for when I went out to the *chicken* house at night."

"How many times did you set the place afire?" Ted asked.

"Never," Father snapped. "I just had it for—ah—emergencies." He squirmed as we all looked at him and his little miner's-lamp foolishness, and he knew we knew that he had never once used it. And then another box floated within reach and Ted landed it with the broom.

This box was larger than the lamp box had been, about the size box half a dozen shirts come in. It was waterlogged, too, and even if Father had wished to keep its contents secret, they were revealed as the box gave way when he reached for it. He stood holding a stack of—something. The top something was made of white linen with a black pencil-line check in half-inch squares, and underneath it was something in a light gray material with a small gold fleur-de-lis design. And there were two or three others in gay patterns. We could see some pearl buttons on them. "Vests," Father said tightly when Ted demanded to know what spendthrift purchase this had been.

None of us had in all our lives seen such dressy vests. "Where did you ever wear them?" Pat asked wonderingly.

Father fidgeted. "When I went out," he said. "They were all the rage."

Ted fingered the material of one. "What'd they cost?" he asked darkly, but Father was saved the embarrassment of dodging; another of his boxes came floating home, and Ted steered it into port.

This was a wooden box cigars had come in, so it was in good shape. "Heavens to Betsy," Ted murmured, looking inside. He lifted out a disk about the size of a nickel, attached to a silver-plated handle as long as his forefinger. Speechlessly he held it aloft. We all looked at Father, who was growing purplish about the face.

"It's a signet," he said between his teeth. On the disk were his initials, E.O.K., in reverse in a monogram design. "You melted a little wax and then stamped it with the signet," he said. There were sticks of wax in the box, too—red, gray, and blue ones. We gazed on the symbols of Father's giddy, frittering youth.

"*Why* did you melt the wax?" Ted asked at last.

"To *seal* things," Father rasped. "Envelopes and things."

"Envelopes!" Ted cried. "Didn't you have gummed flaps in the olden days?"

"It was probably just to give a nice personal touch to letters, Ted," Pat said hastily as Father's jaw muscles bulged.

"Whoops—here comes another one," Ted said, and grabbed up his broom. The box he brought in was the last one. If there were others in Father's wardrobe they had mercifully sunk out of sight before we could rescue them. But the last box made up for anything we may have missed. It revealed a facet of Father's character we had not known existed; he had not only been a spendthrift and a dude—he had also once been musical. Ted reached into the last box. "Would you look at this great big enormous ukulele!" he exclaimed.

Father's teeth gritted. "That's a guitar," he said, "and give it here."

"You *played* this thing?" Ted cried, and twanged it. A deep and moody zonging came forth. "Hey, it still works," Ted said. "Were you in a band?"

"No, not a band," Father said testily. "There were just three of us. We just played for fun." He looked at us defensively. There was disbelief in our faces, for of all people Father seemed the least musical. In church he held an open hymnal and uttered no sound; he never sang in the shower bath; he didn't even whistle while he worked.

Ted spoke for the three of us. "Let's hear you play something once," he said, and held out the guitar.

Father slowly took it. He set his other souvenirs on the steps and seemed to be trying to remember how one held a guitar. At length he got it braced against one knee and brushed his right hand over the strings while he tried out different positions on the neck with the fingers of his left

hand. The guitar made somber noises. "What are you playing?" Ted asked at last.

"I'm not playing anything," Father said hotly. He was perspiring about the forehead. "It isn't in tune," he said suddenly. "I remember now——"

"We've got a piano," Ted said. "Can't you tune it with that? Or do you remember how?"

Father got a hunted look. "Yes, yes," he muttered, "of course I remember how." He yanked the guitar around. "You turn these keys," he said, and took hold of one. Perhaps it was rusted. It resisted him and he gave it a savage twist. Its string broke with a startling, twangy snap, making us all jump, and there was a splash.

"Hey—you dropped it!" Ted yelled. He grabbed for his broom, but Father was more or less in the way, and the guitar was borne off out of reach on the current. "I'll wade after it," Ted said, starting to, but Father seized him with a grip of steel. "I just thought of something," he said, hauling Ted up the stairs. "Let's get out of here, everybody—this water has certainly put out the pilot light on the water heater, and this basement must be full of gas!"

We left the guitar swimming around the basement, to its utter ruin. Father didn't ever have to play it, for by the time the water had drained away the next morning the guitar had become warped and unglued. The basement did not fill with gas, however. My wife, it seemed, had thought of this danger earlier in the evening and had telephoned the gas company to shut off its main line.

"Why didn't you say so?" I asked when she revealed this to me privately. "We could have saved his guitar."

"Yes, I know," she said, and paused. "But to tell you the truth, I thought the evening had already been quite hard enough on him," she murmured. "And besides—it was the only time I ever saw him throw something away, and I think it ought to be encouraged."

# 14.   *Garbled Goblins*

"Maybe this year Halloween will be different," Ted said to me in late October. "Maybe after making a monkey of himself the night of the great flood Dad won't be so bullheaded about Halloween for once."

"Maybe," I said. "He may be embarrassed to, in front of Pat. It'd be nice to spend one Halloween in a house instead of a fortress." Our father had always approached Halloween like an embattled mouse stalking the neighborhood cat. All the other days of the year he was a reasonably optimistic fellow, but on Halloween he expected nothing but the most outrageous behavior from every tot within range. It often made me wonder what he had been up to when he was a boy.

His defense against the little villains was simple but exhaustingly complete; he picked up and carried inside everything outside that was loose. This was an impressive job in a house that had been accumulating possessions for better than a quarter century and seldom throwing anything away. It took about three evenings of hard work after dinner with all hands helping, and on Halloween evening itself, Father blacked out the house and bade everyone lay low. My wife was not used to this attitude, I knew, for she had spoken of Halloween in terms of ducking for apples, popping corn, and other jollity when she was a child.

A few days before Halloween, Father spoke up at the dinner table, addressing Ted and me. "I'd like a hand with the pot plants this evening," he said.

Ted and I had agreed on a strategy of stupidity. "What's the matter with the pot plants?" Ted said.

"They're *outside*," Father said, ruffling right up.

"No frost predicted," I said.

"I'm not talking about frost," Father snapped. "Don't you know Friday's *Halloween?*"

Ted and I exchanged pained looks across the table. "The goblins again," I said.

"What's all this about?" Pat demanded, and Ted and I spoke up before Father could.

"The evil spirits are very bad in this neighborhood," I said, and Ted informed her that we hid under the bed every Halloween and said the Lord's Prayer backward.

"Don't be sacrilegious," Father roared at him. "It's merely a case of taking common-sense precautions," he said to Pat. "I bring in whatever is outside that might be stolen or hurt."

"The pot plants, the screens, the garden hose," I said.

"The door mats, porch light bulbs, lawn furniture," Ted chanted.

"Spade, rake, wheelbarrow," I said. "The house number, awning, letter holder. . . ." Pat's eyes were wide.

"All right, all right," Father said sternly. He turned to Pat. "How would you like to find the pot of Boston ferns pitched right through the front-door glass and slivers all over the rug?"

"It happened to you?" she cried.

"Or the lawn mower on the roof?" he inquired.

"They did that?" she exclaimed.

"Or the rubber door mat stuffed down the chimney and the house full of smoke?"

"No!" she said. "They didn't really?"

"Or the doorknobs tied to piled-up lawn furniture on the porches? Or the hose shoved in a window and turned on?" Ted and I were listening with mild interest. We were familiar with the incidents. Father had culled them from newspapers and tales told him by joky friends over the years. He had dozens of them on tap. But somehow Pat got the idea that he was talking about our immediate neighborhood and things he had witnessed.

"That isn't fun—that's just plain vandalism," she said, and joined Father's campaign. She didn't know what she was in for. When Father stripped the premises he stopped short of rolling up the lawn, but that was about all. Twenty-two potted plants were carried to the basement and placed on a heavy-duty stand built like a flight of steps. The pots included two large stone jardinieres that even child weight lifters could hardly have budged. The other things were stored in appointed places, either in the garage or in the basement and in a regular order Father had worked out. Some items, such as the birdbath, were restored to outside after Halloween, but most things stayed stored till spring, forcing everyone to walk sideways all winter in the more crowded storage areas. This aspect began to bother Pat, and by the third evening, Halloween itself, she felt that Father was overdoing it.

He was then gathering up a row of sponge rocks he had lined the back walk with. "They might throw 'em," he said as he puffed past her with a boxful, basement bound. "They," as she now knew, meant the little devils who even now were doubtless trying on their masks and sheets.

"It seems to me we have to stop somewhere," she said to me. "If they'd throw these big rocks, what's to stop them from throwing the driveway gravel?"

"Good Lord, don't mention that to Dad," I said. "He's never thought of bringing in the gravel."

"Well, you see what I mean," she said. "I don't understand why there are so many bratty kids in this neighborhood anyway. In fact, I haven't seen many kids around here at all, and those I have seen are all right."

"I think they are," I said. "Of course, it's Dad's theory that they've never done any damage only because he has removed all opportunity."

She looked hard at me. "But I thought—the lawn mower on the roof? The door mat in the chimney? The ferns thrown——"

"I guess those things happened *somewhere*. But not around here. He didn't say they did, if you recall."

She looked a little miffed. "Well, I certainly got the impression . . ." She bit her lip. "Touché," she said, and laughed briefly.

Father came hustling out of the basement and hurried out to the garage to drape dustcloths at the windows. He reasoned that this would foil prospective mischief-makers by indicating the garage stored dustcloths, not cars. He snapped a padlock on the door as he finished and made a quick rounding of the grounds to see if he had overlooked any bets. If he hadn't felt the Government might object, I think he would have uprooted the mailbox standing at the curb and stowed it in the basement. Everything seemed in order, so he came into the house to conduct the ceremony of Nobody Home, as Ted and I called it. This was a matter of locking all windows and doors, pulling down shades, and turning out lights. Pat was now in the kitchen fixing dinner, so she didn't know about this phase of the preparations until Father appeared before her, bearing a small lamp which he set on the kitchen table. She was baking a pumpkin pie for dessert and she glanced hastily over her shoulder at the lamp. "What's that for?" she asked.

Father took a moment to inhale the delicious fragrance of the pie. "On Halloween," he said, "we always eat in the kitchen." He went upstairs to pull blinds, leaving her absolutely baffled. "I thought he *hated* to eat in the kitchen," she said to me.

"He does," I told her, "but a light here can't be seen from

the front of the house, in case the blinds aren't absolutely tight."

She glanced about, fidgeting. The kitchen blinds were all pulled, too, and the door locked. "It's getting like a cave in here," she said, "and I can't stand caves."

To me the sealed-off kitchen felt more like a cabin in some mountain fastness, and when all four of us sat down to dinner by the glow of the small lamp, it seemed to me we were like a quartet of conspirators, harking for the arrival of the posse, and prepared to sell our lives dearly. I found myself asking for the potatoes in a hoarse whisper, causing Pat to vibrate noticeably. Father paid no mind to this; he was listening as well as he could while eating, to pick up any sounds of tricksters outside. None came during the meal, and Pat was about to cut the pie when Father remembered something. He got up from the table in a great hurry, mumbling to himself, and made for the door to the basement. We all stared after him. "Doorbell," he said. "I forgot to unhook it." He turned on the basement light and then on second thought turned it off again, got a flashlight from the hall closet, and descended to the basement. "Safer this way," he said.

Pat looked wildly at Ted and me. "Unhook the *door*bell?"

"He has a theory about that, too," I said. "If he disconnects it, nobody can jam it with a pin——" I was interrupted by a yowl from the basement, Father's voice. A moment later there was another. "Dammit to hell," Father said with feeling.

"That's *electricity* he's fooling with," Pat said.

"Can't get much of a shock from a doorbell," Ted said. Father yipped again. "I'd better give him a hand," Ted said, getting up, "or we'll never get to eat that pie." He felt his way down the basement stairs.

Pat laid down a knife she had picked up. "I'll cut this pie when they get back. Electricity makes me nervous." Her glance flitted about the dungeon. "How long does this last, for heaven's sake?"

"Till Halloween's over."

"But that's all night!"

As I nodded the basement party was heard from again. This time there was a metallic clatter and then two yips. My wife jumped and almost turned on the ceiling light. Then Ted called to me. "I dropped the flashlight," he bawled up the stairway. "Bring some matches."

I got a matchbook from my pocket and went to the cellar doorway. "I'll be careful not to set the house afire," I said before Pat could say it. "That's all we need," she was muttering as I went down the dark basement stairs.

Down below, I lighted a match. "Quick," I said. "I've only got three matches, it turns out." Father snorted, almost blowing the first match out.

"Hold it right here," he said. "We almost had it figured out when he dropped the damn flashlight." We all peered up at the little black doorbell box fastened to a joist. "Near as I remember it," Father said, "you unscrew all these brass knob things——"

"I think you only have to unscrew one," I said.

"That's what I've been telling him," Ted said. "Do you know which one?"

"This one, maybe," I said, tapping it. Father jumped. The doorbell had sounded upstairs.

"Don't *ring* it," he said.

"I didn't know that would ring it," I said. "All I did was touch this——"

The doorbell pealed forth a second time. "There you go again," Father cried.

My match went out and I dropped it. "I didn't even touch the thing that time," I said in the darkness. There was a noise upstairs.

"What's that?" Father asked.

"Sounds like footsteps," I said. "Living room."

"Sounds like a team of horses," Ted said.

"Good Lord," Father said and started rapidly feeling his way for the staircase, bumping things. I lighted a match, and Ted and I followed him up.

The kitchen was still dimly lighted, but in the living room lights blazed. Pat was in there—and so also were some small figures in masks and old clothes too big for them. There were only three of them and no horses. The noise was from a jig they were doing for Pat, but they stopped when we three appeared and seemed seized with bashfulness. "I think they're the Baylor children down the block," Pat told us, causing great giggling among them. "I'll be right back with something for you, kids," she said, and left we three great men standing there looking down at the three tots. They seemed hardly worth the trouble of dragging even one pot plant to the basement, let alone purging the whole outside till the place looked from the street like a fugitive who had disguised himself shaving off ears and eyebrows and stripping down to tights.

Pat returned with three triangles wrapped in waxed paper and handed them to the children. "Was that our pie?" Father asked me hoarsely as it left.

"Some of it," I said.

Pat closed the door and rejoined us. "I heard the doorbell," she said lightly, "and you know how it is—when you hear a doorbell, you automatically go to the door."

Father looked scuttled. "They'll spread the word," he mumbled. "We'll have every kid in the neighborhood here now."

"Well, that won't be so many," Pat said, counting on her fingers, "but since I haven't got anything else for them, I'd better cut the rest of that pie in smaller slices." Father gave her a wounded look. He had sometimes done without dessert because there wasn't any dessert, but never before had his dessert been snatched out right from under his twitching nose.

"If you'd care for a prune," Ted said to him, "I've got a box of them in my desk."

Father turned on his heel. "I'm going to bed," he said. With the recklessness of despair he turned on the hall light and stamped on upstairs in its blaze. We turned on the lights downstairs, and Pat sliced up the rest of the pumpkin pie into a lot of finger wedges, but only one more bunch of children showed up during the evening. Apparently Father had convinced most of the neighborhood small fry that time spent on him was time wasted, and when we turned out the lights for the night, there were still ten fingers of pumpkin pie left. To make the arithmetic simpler, we put a finger in the refrigerator for Father's breakfast and divided the rest evenly between us.

## 15. *Father and the Merry-Christmas-Go-Round*

Christmas was looming on the horizon when I happened to recall something. "We gave ourselves six months," I reminded Pat, "when we decided to try living with Father. Remember?"

"I'd almost forgotten," she said. "And it's past six months now."

It was, and I wondered if it proved anything except that Father was no bargain to live with. "Maybe we aren't such bargains for *him* to live with," Pat said abruptly. "When we're his age, we may think people our age are difficult." This sounded revolutionary if not treasonous. "I think he's been having some hard knocks lately," she went on, sounding almost like Father himself. "Maybe just once we ought to try and see things from his point of view. After all, Christmas is coming."

"You put your finger on it," I said. "Father loves Christmas. Nothing would please him more than for us to let him run the whole show."

"Then let's," she said. "Teddy too." I passed the word along to Ted, who winced. "This'll be the white-tree Christmas," he said.

For years Father had been sniping at the traditional green Christmas tree, ever since he had seen one sprayed with white paint in a downtown window display. The novelty had entranced him and he had been stunned and hurt at the stony opposition he had run into at home that year when he suggested we switch to a white tree. We had not switched, and though he had not given up the campaign, cranking it up each December all over again, he probably didn't expect to get anywhere, particularly this year when facing a new united front of three adult children, each one more old-fashioned than the next, in his eyes. He even brought it up in a defeatist manner.

"I guess we'll pick up the same old Norway spruce somewhere for our tree this year," he remarked. "No use talking about anything with a little life to it, I suppose."

Pat, the uninitiated, spoke up. "Like what, Dad?"

He glanced warily toward Ted and me. "Well, if you want to see something pretty," he said, "you ought to see a *white* Christmas tree some time. Snow white."

"That sounds lovely," Pat said promptly, and gave Ted and me a meaningful look. "*Doesn't* it?"

"I guess we could try it for once," I said, or maybe Ted did. Grudging as it was, the remark overjoyed Father. He slapped his hands on his knees. "Now we're getting somewhere," he said heartily. "I'll start keeping my eye out. Some places have better ones than other places." We could almost hear his brain shifting into high gear. "We'll need some new ornaments, too," he said, "and new lights. Maybe all blue. Say—now wouldn't that be beautiful?" He was looking straight ahead and far away, and his eyes were the eyes of a man who sees a vision.

One reason Father so adored Christmas was that he was a naturally secretive man. Christmas gave him the chance to have all kinds of extra secrets, and he certainly made the most of it. And since he also dearly loved to spend money, he had a glorious time each year buying present after present and hiding them away till Christmas Day. He didn't go in for fancy wrappings at all, though. He bought nearly everything at Famous-Barr, and when he handed you a present you got it in Famous-Barr's slate-gray wrapping paper and tied with heavy white twine. Inside it there was a charge-account sales slip with the price written on it, and Father's System was to stand near and snatch it out before you could read it as you opened the gift. This added zing to Christmas morning.

It was still two weeks till Christmas, and while Father hurried about, assembling presents in his stealthy way and looking into the white-tree question, the rest of us tried to figure out what on earth to buy for him.

"He's pretty impossible," Ted said. "He wants everything, so you'd think it ought to be easy to buy him something. But he's already got it, so where are you?"

Pat, remembering what had happened when she shopped for Father's birthday, was not now so willing to rush in. "If we all think hard," she said, "maybe we can think of one nice thing we can give him from all three of us."

"If we do his Christmas will be ruined," I said. "He always wants a lot of packages to open. At least a dozen."

Ted nodded, and she stared at us. "But—how do you give him a lot of presents when right now we can't think of even one?"

"I'm not sure now myself," I said, "but we always managed. Of course, he didn't like most of them."

"But he liked getting them," Ted said. "You can't have everything."

"The one thing you can be sure of pleasing him with is a thermometer," I said. "We can each give him a thermometer, so that's three presents."

"Just a minute," Pat said. "There's already about fifteen thermometers in this house. Maybe twenty. I never *saw* a house with so many thermometers." This was true, but it made no difference.

"Thermometers appeal to him," I said. "It doesn't matter even if you give him one for a place where he's already got one. He'll put it there and then watch them to see how much difference there is in their readings."

"I think I'll give him a clinical thermometer," Ted said. "I can get it wholesale, and he may as well get started on them."

"Don't worry about it," I said to Pat, who was looking frustrated. "We always manage to accumulate a boxful of stuff for him by Christmas. Just remember—it's quantity that counts."

It may seem strange that we had never simply taken to asking Father what he wanted for Christmas, thus settling the question and putting him on notice not to buy it for himself. The reason was, he demanded that we surprise him. In turn he insisted on surprising us. It was all right to drop subtle hints, such as letting him see you inspecting moth holes in a sweater you'd like replaced, but to tell him you needed a sweater took away from him all the pleasure of buying it.

A week before Christmas he decided on the sunroom for the Christmas tree. In other years he had picked spots in the living room, as he liked to look at the tree from his easy chair. It seemed peculiar that this year, when he would finally have the white tree he had been pining for, he was going to stick it clear out in the sunroom. His reason dawned on us when we saw him trying the lock on the sunroom doors.

The doors had never been closed since the house was built, being one more of the frills Father's builder had added, and now Father discovered that the lock didn't work. We could hear him swearing under his breath as he tried to force the key, and Ted had a look at it. "The bolt misses the keeper by a quarter inch," he announced. Father swore

some more. "If you're bent on locking it," Ted said, "I'll pull the pins and take the door on this side down to the workbench where I can do it right." Ever since he had taken manual training at high school Ted was a stickler on proper tools and correct procedure. Father's slap-dash carpentering was quite a contrast to this professional approach. "Never mind, never mind," he muttered, loping off to the basement. "I haven't got time for all that." He came back with nothing but a screwdriver. He took off the bolt keeper with it, squinted hard at the hole in the wood behind it, and attacked it vigorously, using the screwdriver as a chisel. Ted made a strangling sound and Father reddened but finished his chiseling and tried the lock. It closed now and that was good enough for him. He didn't bother to reposition the keeper but took it to the basement with his screwdriver for future attention.

"I could've done as well with my teeth," Ted said to me, examining the hole Father had made. "He split the wood. Well, after Christmas I'll do the job right."

Satisfied that he was in business, Father took over the sun-room, shoving the wicker furniture around to make room for his tree-to-come, pulling all the blinds down for secrecy, and assembling ornaments from the attic. He had taken charge of the tree every year, but I had never known him to spend half the time it seemed to be taking this year. "I can understand it," Pat said. "It's like a new dress."

"It's just a Christmas tree," I said, "only a different color." So I thought. So thought we all. We shrugged at Father's busyness with the affair of the tree and went on accumulating gifts for him as ideas came. We had thought of several more, and Pat was easier in her mind.

"Yardsticks," Ted had said, fetching home two free ones from a hardware store on Delmar Boulevard. To give them richness he varnished them. Though she knew Father already had yardsticks all over the house, Pat had now learned the routine. "Oh yes, he likes lots of yardsticks," she said, and so alerted, she added another present to the pile by making with some red cotton cloth a sort of sack an inch wide and three feet long. She called it a yardstick holder.

I browsed around downtown on my noon hours and picked up a few other things such as an automatic pencil that wrote in three colors, a magnetized paper-clip holder, and a magnifying glass with a battery in the handle to light a little bulb. "I haven't any idea," I told Pat when she asked what Father wanted with such a thing, "but I know it's the kind of present he's more apt to like than handkerchiefs or socks." She got the idea and swiftly bought him a toenail clipper, an electric necktie presser, and a silver money clip with his initials on it.

We counted up everything we had for him and they came to twenty items, counting Ted's two yardsticks separately. He had also got the clinical thermometer, a weather forecaster in the form of a Hansel and Gretel cottage to hang on a wall, and he had tooled some strips of leather for bookmarks, not because Father was an avid reader but because he had the leather on hand.

During this time Father had been hauling home his usual parcels and whisking them off to his closet for hiding, but not all the packages he brought home this year went up there. Some he carried to the sunroom, hiding them from us en route by holding them on his off side, as if we had X-ray vision. Several were bulky, and one was heavy enough to make him walk with his knees bent. We decided he was buying so many presents he had run out of closet space.

The Christmas tree itself Father brought home in the dark of the night so we couldn't see it, on December 23, and requested that we go upstairs and not peek while he carried it in. This struck Ted and me as pretty odd.

"What's so secret about it?" Ted asked me, and I agreed that if you had seen one white Christmas tree you had seen them all. "And this business about locking the sunroom," he said suspiciously. "Just to trim a tree?" We looked long at each other. "I wonder," Ted murmured, "what he's *really* got in there?"

The remark planted a doubt that nibbled at our minds. Yet Father certainly went through the motions of trimming a tree the next day, Christmas Eve. He spent the whole afternoon at it and all the evening, behind the sunroom's closed doors. He took a radio along, to keep him company, we supposed, and it roared out Christmas music while he worked. He finished at about eleven P.M. and went off to bed after locking the sunroom doors. He looked surprisingly chipper, as if his labors had refreshed him, though the rest of us were exhausted from wrapping presents, mostly his.

Ted and I stopped in the kitchen for a bite to eat on the way to bed. Pat had baked so many Christmas cookies that she had temporarily lost her appetite for snacks. She went on upstairs and Ted and I made baked-bean sandwiches and took them to the dining room. Ted's eyes strayed to the sunroom doors as we munched. They were glass doors but not the kind you could see through, except that you could tell light and dark. "Blue lights, he said," Ted remarked. "Did you happen to see any blue light through that glass while he was in there?"

"Come to think of it, I didn't see *any* light," I said, and we stepped over to the doors. "No wonder," Ted said. "He seems to have newspapers or something thumbtacked to the other side."

He gave the knob of the locked doors a little pull. Lacking a keeper, the lock seemed pretty flimsy. "Testing," Ted said, pulling again. With a slight sound of splintering wood the doors abruptly came open and we stood peering into the sunroom. Neither of us spoke for a few moments. "Am I imagining things," Ted said at last in a croak, "or is that——"

"Yep," I said. "It sure is. A *pink* Christmas tree. Not white. Pink."

We stepped cautiously into the sunroom and I felt of a branch. "It isn't a real tree. Feels silky and fluffed up."

Ted seemed to have lost his voice. He was slowly looking the tree up and down. It was quite a creation, putting me somewhat in mind of a Maypole. Also of that spun-sugar candy you see at carnivals. Somehow it brought butterflies to mind too. It was the most versatile Christmas tree I ever saw, and if you closed one eye and concentrated on its shape, it suggested Christmas as well. "Mercy on us all," Ted murmured. He stooped, and I saw he had found the cord to the electric outlet. "Might as well see what it looks like lighted," he said, and shoved in the plug.

The effect was stunning. Instantly the pink tree lighted up in a blaze of blue lights. Then the blue lights began winking, on and off, on and off. At the very top there was a crystal star shimmering with light. All the ornaments were new and were either white or silver. And this was not all.

"Hey," Ted said, "this thing's moving." It was indeed. The tree was pirouetting like a dancer. Now it even looked like a dancer. And yet this still was not all.

To light, color, and motion Father's tree now added sound. From what we had supposed was merely a big box on which it was standing there suddenly blared music—"Deck the Hall with Boughs of Holly"—appallingly loud and clear in the quiet night.

Ted sprang at the plug and yanked it from the socket. We stood petrified for a moment and then quickly tiptoed out of the sunroom and stood listening. There was no sound from upstairs. Father slept. Ted fixed the sunroom doors with a little chewing gum, so they looked to be locked if you didn't jerk them. "No point in spoiling his fun," he muttered. "That's right," I said. "He gets such a lot out of Christmas. Tomorrow morning we'll have to pretend this is all a big surprise."

It was not very hard to pretend surprise Christmas morning. By then I was half convinced Ted and I had been too tired the night before to see Father's tree well or that the artificial light had given the illusion of pinkness. And when

Father flung open the sunroom doors and we saw the tree in its magnificence, twirling and singing, we really were surprised. With daylight to help, the tree was about five times as pink as it had seemed the night before. And the blinking blue lights were blinkier and bluer, and the underneath music was louder. To look stunned was hardly any trouble at all, especially for Pat, who had no warning, and that was good enough for Father. He gave us credit for knowing overpowering beauty when we saw it, and if it left us almost speechless for the time being, that was understandable.

Gifts, after such glory, were almost an anticlimax. Nonetheless the assortment we had worked up for Father scored remarkably well. His favorite was the money clip, and I suppose the Hansel and Gretel cottage was the next, but there was nothing he did not like at least a little bit, which was a record.

For the three of us he had found time between tree shopping to buy thirty or forty gifts, if you counted the jokes he always worked in, such as a penny box of matches in a cigar-lighter box before he gave you the real lighter. Though he was never concerned about selecting practical gifts, it happened that one of those he gave Pat was just what she had been needing—an electric mixer, as she had discovered when making Christmas cookies. "I overheard you saying how much you wished you had a mixer," he told her, "and it was the very first present I bought."

"Do you mean it was right here in the house while I was struggling with all those cookies?" she cried. She had baked something like five or six hundred of them, not having had much experience at estimating the yield of any given amount of dough.

"The whole time," he said happily. "It was right upstairs in my closet."

"Well, why didn't you give it to me *then?*" she asked. "When I was needing it so?"

He looked at her with shock. "You mean—would I give you a Christmas present *before* Christmas?" he gasped. "You bet your sweet life I wouldn't. Why, what kind of a Christmas would that be?"

For Father it wouldn't have been Christmas at all. In that respect he was a traditionalist, pink tree or no pink tree.

# 16. *Father, Financial Wizard*

Some time during the spring it began to dawn on Father that he was saving money. This was partly because he had got a raise and partly because Pat and I were sharing his household expenses. For him to save money was highly unusual. He was always interested in making money, but though he claimed he was equally interested in saving it, he had never managed to do so before. In fact he had given up trying and in recent years had taken a sort of martyr's pleasure in admitting he was helpless in the grip of his spendthriftiness.

Counting up now, he was astonished to find that a nest egg had crept up on him. He was carrying almost a thousand dollars more in his checking account than he was used to having. He was so pleased that he let the cat out of the bag, though ordinarily he kept such intelligence strictly to himself. He was immediately sorry he had said anything. None of we three had the least sympathy with his squandering, and we all spoke up.

"I suppose you'll blow it on clothes," I said.

"Fritter it, more than likely," Ted said, "and won't have anything to show for it at all."

"Well, it seems to me that here's a wonderful chance to finally save something, Dad," Pat said, "before anything happens to it."

Her advice was the least ruffling. "I *am* going to save it," he said. "At least," he added, "I'm going to do something constructive with it." He thought about this for two or three seconds. "I'll open a special account for it," he said.

It was his system to separate his money according to ultimate use by keeping it in different bank accounts. He had one he called the Vacation Account and another he called the New Car Account, besides others I didn't know about. This was in addition to his regular checking account, giving his bank, Bremen Trust Company, the giddy feeling it had many more customers than it really did.

I suppose the fact we had now all heard about this new extra money of his made Father comparatively chatty about it, and a day later he announced he had set up what he called his Investment Account with it. "I'm going to keep my eye out for a good thing," he said. "I've missed out on a lot of opportunities in my life because I didn't have the liquid assets for equity financing."

His words had a haunting ring in my ears. During my boyhood life at home had been punctuated by Father's investments, all of them doggedly opposed by my mother. The companies he put money into were companies nobody had heard about before, almost as if they had sprung into life at a whiff of some money burning a hole in Father's pocket. Even the businesses they were in, or supposed to be in, were never anything dull and profitable, such as making soap or pickles. One and all they were exciting and often exotic, involving treasure from the earth, tropical riches, and luxury. Mines seemed most popular with him—gold, silver, and even lead—and there was an oil well or two, a fur farm, a banana plantation, and so on. He got a lot out of the ventures but not any money. Without exception he lost his entire investment in each and never collected a dime in dividends that I knew of.

"How about A.T.&T.?" I said. "Everybody uses telephones, and the company pays dividends on its common as regularly as bonds."

Father gave me a sharp, uneasy look. Up till now whenever he had discussed an investment at home it had been with my mother, who thought all stocks were dangerous, if not wicked. "They're too big," he said of American Telephone, and declined to go into it farther. However, I knew that what he really objected to was not the company's size but its stability and the piddling 6 per cent or so he could get. He wanted risk and visions of fabulous gains.

"Well," I said, "a good industrial, like General Motors——"

"Never mind," he said rather testily. "I know all about that. If I'd had a few thousand to put in G.M. twenty years ago, that would've been different. I'd be a millionaire today. What I'm hunting for is a small new outfit with the same kind of big prospects."

It was what he had been hunting for all his life. It was possible he had even had a chance to buy into General Motors in its infancy, and if so, my guess is that he chose instead a company being formed to revolutionize the passenger-balloon industry.

It didn't take Father very long to find the investment he was looking for. I suppose he was on a good many mailing lists, resulting from his previous plunges. The offering that took his fancy was, at least, less exotic than the earlier ones. "It's something that's going to sweep the country," he told us. "A line of concentrated foods. All the restaurants and hotels will be customers first thing—they'll save labor and overhead, see?—and then we'll go after the retail market. This is the biggest thing in years."

"What do you mean, concentrated food?" Ted asked. "Like bouillon cubes?"

"Not like that," Father said. "I can't explain all the technical details, but a tablespoon equals a pound of fresh. It makes a kind of pudding when you add water. Meat puddings, fruit puddings, egg puddings, vegetable——"

"I wouldn't like them," Ted said. Father glowered at him. Negative thinking drove him wild.

"You haven't even tasted any," he shouted. "It's the most convenient thing ever invented. It's a milestone in the history of food. You can store it indefinitely. Think of the market among campers alone." Having never gone camping except with the Home Guards in his younger days, Father didn't appreciate that cooking over a campfire was one of the reasons for going camping and that a tablespoon of pudding powder was no substitute for a steak or even for a frankfurter.

"I'd like to see some of this stuff," Ted said darkly. "You sure these jokers know about the Pure Food and Drug Act?"

"What's it called, Dad?" Pat asked in a hurry to head off the explosion he was about to fire at Ted.

"Delly-Con-Nootie," Father said. None of us peeped for a few moments and he looked defensively about. "Stands for Delicious, Convenient, and Nutritious," he said. "*I* think it's very catchy."

"Well," I said at last, "I don't imagine they'll run into any copyright infringements. There *can't* be anything else on the market with a name like that."

"That's a good point," Father said, favoring me with a nod. "Shows they're on their toes."

The Delly-Con-Nootie people showed one evidence of good faith right away. They gave the investors some free samples of the product. Father had seldom been offered any samples by his other companies, and never by the gold mines, so this gesture bolstered his conviction he had finally latched onto something superb. He brought the samples home and spread them out on the kitchen table for everyone to admire. They were commercial looking and contained in small brown paper packets about the size of garden-seed envelopes. I had expected something gaudy from an enterprise named Delly-Con-Nootie, and I felt a little less skeptical of Father's investment. He did not say how much he had put into the company, but since he had a thousand dollars, that seemed answer enough. The stock, he had told us, was being offered at two dollars a share, and he always preferred a lot of little shares to a few big ones.

"Let's try some for dinner," he said to Pat. "It's simple and quick to use—two of our big selling points. How about this Peachie Creem?"

She looked at the Peachie Creem, a dessert mix, and read the directions. "This only makes a pint," she said. "That won't be enough to go——"

"You can pass me up," Ted said promptly. "That'll stretch it."

Father did not dignify this carping with a reply. "Mix up a few of the other dessert ones too," he told Pat. "Let's have plenty—there's all kinds. 'A pantry in a handful.'" He watched us to see the effect of the phrase. "Pretty nifty, hey?" he said. "That's one of our slogans."

Pat, looking rather owlish about it, went ahead and stirred up some of the samples, in boiling water as directed. "It says you can use milk if a richer product is desired," she said, reading labels.

"I don't desire a richer product," I said. "Let's make it prove what it can do."

She set aside the dessert she had been planning to serve and, when the time came, brought heaped dessert bowls of the Delly-Con-Nootie to the table. There was quite a bit of it. It had a semi-jelled consistency, and Father rubbed his hands together in anticipation. "Excuse me," Ted said, starting to leave the table, but Pat detained him. "I think you ought to try some," she said, "but if you feel that way about it, you can have some of the other dessert." She passed to Father, herself, and me the bowls of Delly-Con-Nootie and brought Ted a helping of the other dessert. It was blackberry cobbler, the crust golden and flaky, topped with whipped cream.

"Well, here's to success," Father said, as if he was about to have a drink, and spooned up some of his dessert. "Delicious," he said the instant it was in his mouth.

Pat took a spoonful and then another. "I don't think I've ever tasted anything exactly like it before," she said after rolling her eyes to the ceiling and thinking it over. I put off commenting for the time being.

Ted, tearing into his luscious cobbler, studied all our faces, especially Father's. "What would you say it reminds you of most?" he inquired, as a scientist among the primitives.

Father spoke up. "Tastes very much like a delicious sort of —ah . . ." He stopped and looked at Pat. "Mine's the peach, isn't it?"

"You have some of each," she said. "I divided it—peach, cherry, orange, and coconut."

"Oh yes," Father said, "I see now. They're different colors." They were a little different, in a good light. They were pastel colors, blending easily into each other.

I swamped around in my dish. "I suppose the whitest is the coconut."

"Cherry, isn't it?" Pat murmured, tasting hard.

Father located his whitest section and tried it. "Vanilla," he announced, but Pat reminded him that there wasn't any vanilla-flavored sample among them.

We all three spooned about our dishes for a while, slowly rolling on our tongues dabs from widely separated areas of our bowls. I tried closing my eyes and it helped bring out a latent chemical flavor I had begun to notice in all the varieties. Once you isolated the chemical flavor you couldn't get away from it, and my eyes wandered to Father's bowl. He was manfully going on down to the bottom, occasionally uttering a "Very good" and once a half-strangled "Yum, yum," when noticing Ted lapping up the last of his cobbler.

"I'll serve the other samples during the week if you like, Dad," Pat said as he rose from the table. He looked a bit doughy, I thought.

"Fine," he said, and paused thoughtfully. "I think the helpings could be smaller, though," he said. "A good deal smaller.

It's a very filling food." He went off to his easy chair and cigar, one hand clamped to his stomach.

I didn't finish my bowl, nor did Pat. Not that we distrusted the stuff—it was harmless, I'm sure—but aside from its sameness there was the persistent chemical flavor. If Father noticed this, he didn't admit it, and he ate through all the samples on hand with virtually no help after the first go-around. I had seen in myself a tendency to ignore the faults of things I owned or wanted to approve of, and now I decided I came by it honestly. Father not only smacked his lips over Delly-Con-Nooties and envisioned lucky diners all over the country soon doing the same—he now did something else that bespoke his faith, a rash and impulsive move with a built-in debacle. He brought it up the following week.

"I've got a chance to buy a few more shares of D.C.N.," he said, "before the price starts shooting up." It took us a few moments to catch onto the initials. They had a crisp financial flavor that the full name somehow lacked.

"Dee Cee Enn?" Ted said, carefully articulating each syllable. "You talking about that Delly-Con-Nootie?" Father nodded shortly. He had not been particularly addressing Ted. "Buy a few *more* shares?" Ted said, sounding as if Father was proposing bankruptcy as a lark.

Father frowned at his tone. "As a matter of fact, I'm thinking mainly of you," he told Ted. "This is an investment to help pay for your medical education."

Ted looked as if Father had lost his marbles. "That does it," he said. "Off to the plumbing shop."

Father ignored him. "I was wondering how you're fixed," he said to Pat and me. "You have something put aside, don't you?"

His question took me by surprise. Personal finances were something we hardly ever discussed, and never in his life had Father borrowed money from me. "Well, we have a savings account," I said. He nodded. "Eighty dollars," I said, "more or less."

"Eighty dollars!" he exclaimed. "Is that all?" In some way Father had got the idea we were saving pots of money by living in his house. The arrangement was that Pat and I paid a certain number of the monthly bills and Father paid the others, and it cost us a little more than it had cost to run our own home. "Well," he said after a few seconds, "it'll buy you forty shares, at least. That's better than nothing."

"Buy *us* forty shares?" I said.

"I'm going to pick up another block of a hundred and fifty," he said. "I'd like to see you get in on this while you can still buy in at two dollars." He lowered his voice slightly. "Next week," he said, "it's figured to jump to five."

"Can we talk it over awhile, Dad?" Pat said before I could tell him that one taste of Delly-Con-Nootie was all I had needed to make up my mind about its future.

"Don't take too much time," he said. "I'll have to know by tomorrow morning."

"He can know right now, as far as I'm concerned," I said to Pat when we went off to talk about it. "Surely you aren't thinking of pouring our dab of money down that rathole?"

"Well, not all of it," she said.

"Not all of it? Not *any* of it."

"Now, listen," she said. "Is your father an easy man to live with?" I shook my head. "Will he be any easier to live with if we act as if he's stupid?" I shook my head. "All right. Isn't it worth something to keep things a little pleasanter around here?"

"You have a point," I said.

"And besides, it's fun to gamble a little."

We discussed it for a few minutes and then went back to give Father the good news. "We've decided to come in on D.C.N. with you, Dad," I said. "We can't afford much, of course, because we don't believe in buying on margin."

"That's sensible," he said heartily. "The great thing is to make a beginning." He whipped out a notebook. "What do you plan to invest?"

"Ten bucks," I said. The notebook fell into his lap. "T-t-ten dollars?" he said hoarsely. "Is *that* all?"

"Five shares," I said. "Right?" He shoved the notebook back into his pocket. "I'll write you a check," I said. "You probably wouldn't want to wait till I can go to the bank and draw the money out of our savings account."

Father wasn't sure that the Delly-Con-Nootie people would even fool around with selling as few as five shares, but they were cheerful about it, possibly as a favor to him. Neither Pat nor I had seen a stock certificate before, and when he brought ours home, we were dazzled. It looked something like money, only bigger, about a foot square, in green and gold, with both our names on it. "If you want, I'll put it in my safe-deposit box," Father said. We had been thinking of framing it.

"I'd like to keep it around awhile so I can look at it," Pat said, and Father smiled at the childish whim. "Just don't lose it," he said. "It's going to be worth a lot of money. Five hundred dollars if the stock hits a hundred."

Delly-Con-Nootie wasn't listed on the New York Stock Exchange, we found out after a while, or on any other exchange so far as we knew. This would have made it difficult to keep up with the quotations except that Father seemed to have his finger on its financial pulse. For a week or so after we bought in the stock hung at $2, according to Father's information. Then one evening he came home smoking a cigar. "She shot up to two dollars and fifty cents," he announced. "A clear twenty-five per cent gain already." He went off to put his hat in the hall closet, walking as if he had springs in his shoes.

"We're worth twelve-fifty," I said to Pat. "Let's take our profit and beat it." As a matter of fact, I don't know how you would have gone about selling your Delly-Con-Nootie shares, except to Father, of course.

Now that the stock had begun to rise, he gave us daily flashes on it. It went quickly from $2.50 to almost $3 and then more slowly to $3.75. At this point it seemed to pause

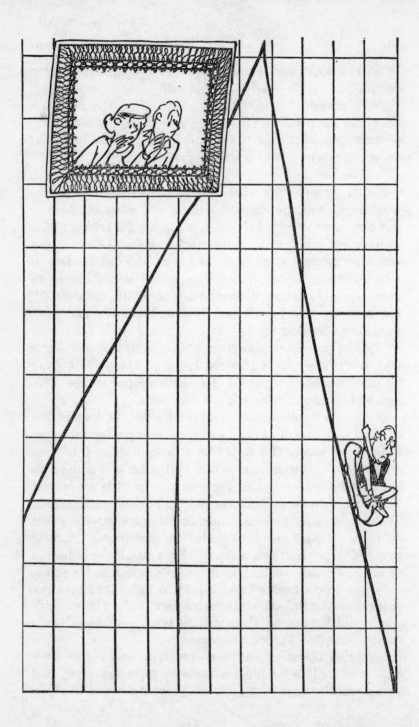

thoughtfully, and Father reported there was some profit taking going on. "Short-term operators," he said, dismissing
them with a brief smile.

He skipped a few days' reports. "Some technical adjust-
ments taking place," he then advised us. "Temporary situation."

"What's the stuff worth now?" Ted asked. He was not included in the investment conversations, but he took as much
interest in the daily fluctuations as if he had risked his wad.

"Two dollars," Father said, since Pat and I were also waiting to hear.

"You mean it's already lost all it gained?" Ted cried.

"It's in a much firmer position now," Father snapped. "A
major cyclical upswing is in the making."

"The panic is on," Ted mumbled. Father looked as if he
could have killed him, but while Ted's financial counsel was
all negative, it was sound. Delly-Con-Nootie went down like
a stone, and after three painful weeks, during which Father
muttered about business indicators and rising trend lines, we
stopped asking what it was worth.

"I hope he didn't borrow any money to buy those extra
hundred and fifty shares," Pat said to me. "Borrowed it from
himself, probably," I said. "His New Car Account probably
got soaked for it. You notice he's stopped talking about when
he's going to trade his old one in."

As a matter of fact, Father even stopped smoking cigars
for a while, but I think this was merely a penance he put
on himself. Personally I thought his humiliation at home was
penance aplenty. He offered to pay Pat and me ten dollars
for our stock, and I guess we should have let him, to save his
face. Instead, with the indelicacy of the young, we said we
wanted to keep the magnificent certificate on view, to remind
us of our foolishness, and he almost bit his pipestem in two
in dismay. For us our ten dollars' worth of Delly-Con-Nootie
proved to be a happy investment, yielding a sort of dividend
for several months by making Father think twice before he
told us what to do, at least sometimes.

# 17. *The Day Father Disowned Me*

For a man of Father's temperament humble pie was almost as bad as strychnine. The weeks that followed his exposure as a financial innocent were hard on him, and while we didn't rub it in, we noticed what a marvelous sense of freedom arose from his new bashfulness toward us. He stopped asking what time we had got to bed if we were out late, almost bit his tongue but kept strict silence when I decided to wear my old straw hat another season, and was mild as milk about some higher than usual bills in his share of the household expenses. This idyl could not have lasted indefinitely, but it still had a lot of mileage left when we accidentally took Father off the hook.

The thing that did it was photography. Ted got interested in it and then I did, and the minute Father got wind of this, he started looking five years younger. The reason was plain: most of our interests were blank walls to him, but photography had been one of his own pet hobbies when he was a young man. His camera had been one called a Pony Premo, with a lens very good for that time—a rapid rectilinear. The camera produced a negative four inches by five on a glass plate, focusing through a ground glass covered by a black cloth. It was now practically a museum piece. "Photography?" he said eagerly when he happened to hear us talking. "Thinking of taking up photography?"

"Have you still got any of your old darkroom stuff, Dad?" Ted asked him. He should have known that once Father had something he always had it.

"You bet," he said, and almost sprang out of his chair. "Finest equipment on the market." He sped like a homing pigeon up to his bedroom and opened a trunk he kept in one corner. There in a box under some Canton flannel alongside a souvenir conch shell just abaft of some old military hairbrushes was his photography equipment, as good as new, almost. Father opened the box himself, hovering over it protectively, and took out his camera. "This is a very fine lens," he said, and turned the camera over several times, apparently hunting for something. As yet we couldn't see the fine lens, for the camera was folded into a leather case about the size of a cigar box. "There's a release button somewhere around —oops," Father said. The front of the box flew open, and there was a gleam of brass and mahogany. Ted and I looked at it curiously. "That's the way you do," Father said. "Then you pull . . . the . . . bellows. . . ." As he talked his fingers were exploring the camera, now and then yanking at things.

"Don't you remember how it works?" Ted said.

"It's a very fine camera," Father said. "I just don't want to force anything——"

"That looks like a latch," Ted said, pointing to a brass hook. Father undid it and opened the camera. "By George," he said as the bellows creaked open. "They don't make cameras like this today."

"They sure don't," Ted said. "Open the shutter and let's have a peek through the back without the ground glass."

Father looked at him tolerantly. "You're not used to good cameras like this one, son," he said. "You see, you *focus* through the ground——"

"I think you've got a leaky bellows," Ted said. "That's what I want to check." Father looked a little insulted and kept firm hold of his camera while Ted examined it.

"Bulb's rotten," Ted said, feeling of the limp little rubber ball that operated the shutter. He worked the shutter by hand a few times. "Spring's weak," he said, and peered through the back of the camera. "Leaks like a sieve," he said. Father's eyes snapped. "But it's repairable," Ted added, "and everything considered, it looks pretty good." Father stopped clouding up. He carefully set the camera down and picked something else out of the equipment box. It seemed to be a bundle of varnished sticks.

"This is my tripod," he said, turning it over and over. The bundle was about a foot and a half long. "Very clever," he said, "the way it all folds up . . . and makes . . . such . . ." He gave the bundle a good shake and it clattered to the floor in three pieces. He swore under his breath.

"Those are the legs," Ted said, and picked one up. "I see," he said. "The top part swings up and the bottom slides down, like this."

"What did I tell you?" Father said. "Simple but clever. Go ahead and set it up."

"Where's the rest of it?" Ted said. Father blinked at him. "You must have a platform to set on top," Ted said. Father peered into his box and lifted out some plate holders and things. "Nothing here," he said. "I don't remember any——"

"You're holding it," Ted said, reaching for a small triangular bit of wood. He snapped the legs into some brackets on it and the tripod stood alone.

At the bottom of the box were the trays Father had used to develop his pictures. They were quaint-looking glass trays with fancy designs on the bottoms, but Ted and I were glad to get them. We bore them off to the basement darkroom we were setting up in the old coalbin. "I think he wants us to use his camera, too," I said to Ted.

"Those enormous negatives?" Ted said. "I can't afford to run the thing. Why don't you?"

As it happened, I had not bought a camera yet and was still practicing with an old box Brownie I had found around the house. "Maybe I will," I said. "I'll see what it costs to fix it." It was a decision of great moment. The consequences to me were unnerving and to Father appalling.

I took the camera downtown, and Schiller's photography shop on Locust Street accepted the repair job as a challenge. They began beating the bushes for rubber squeeze bulbs, which they had run out of twenty-five years before, and set their most venerable repairman to tinkering with the camera while the stock boy probed dusty corners for some glass-plate negatives. It took two weeks and some thirty man-hours before the camera was ready; Schiller's charged most of it off to experience and billed me for only five dollars, though this modest expense didn't surprise Father. "That's because it's built right," he said. "You can bet your sweet life they don't see many cameras like that."

In the meantime Ted had bought himself a miniature camera, a little Foth-Derby. Next to it the overhauled Pony Premo looked as big as a locomotive. Ted could take six pictures and read through the newspaper while I was assembling Father's tripod, screwing his camera onto it, focusing on the ground glass while hiding under a black cloth he had unearthed somewhere, inserting plate holders, testing the shutter speed, stopping down the lens, checking to see if I had remembered to pull the slide from the plate holder. I was so fascinating a sight that Ted spent part of his time taking pictures of me taking pictures.

Father saw nothing amusing about it. So far as he was concerned, Ted's camera was a bauble. Its fast lens and sharp definition over the entire picture area did not impress him. In fact it made him mad, because in a kindly effort to show him an advantage of this Ted took a portrait of Father as he sat reading in his easy chair one evening. The only light was that from the floor lamp beside the chair, and though the negative was a little underexposed, Ted and I thought it an excellent likeness. The part of Father's face that wasn't all shadow had a proud and jowly air; he looked somehing like a statue of Buddha. "Now *there's* definition," Ted said. "Where the light hits, you can see every pore."

"Pores be damned," Father rasped, glaring at the print, which Ted had blown up to five by seven inches on a make-shift enlarger he had built of scraps. "Who wants a picture of his pores?" Without waiting for an answer, he went to burrowing in the photograph drawer of his secretary-desk. A good many of the old photographs there were those he had taken with the camera I was now using, most of them being of groups—women with enormous hats and bosoms, and with dresses to their ankles, and dudes wearing yards of watch

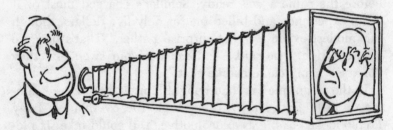

chain across waistcoats, and with slicked-down hair twining about their foreheads. But he couldn't find any close-ups. "I must have given them all away," he said. "People were always after me for them, naturally. I gave away hundreds— and all properly mounted too." He added the last remark as an automatic reproof, mainly to Ted. Ted didn't usually bother dressing up his prints by mounting them, nor did he see any sense in it. I wasn't mounting my pictures either, mainly because of the stately pace at which I was taking them. There weren't enough to fool with yet.

"I think maybe I'll mount this one," Ted said, fondly regarding his shadowy portrait of Father. "It's a nice low-key job."

Father looked pained. "It isn't anything. If you want to take a real portrait, my camera is the——" He stopped and looked at me. "Why don't you try?"

"All right," I said. "When shall I take you?"

"Practice awhile first," he said. "Practice on some other people." It was good advice, perhaps a little rough on the other people, but sound. There didn't *seem* to be overtones of disaster about it, but what happened was not remotely like anything Father had intended.

I bought another boxful of glass-plate negatives from the faithful Schiller's, overjoying their sales manager, and practiced on Pat and Sarah Plim, until they saw the prints. They then told me to find some other models, not caring about how the light hit their noses, or saying I had picked their worst angles, though they agreed the pictures were full of detail and a credit to the lens. I had taken them outside to get plenty of light so that I could stop the lens down for depth of focus—the sort of terms Ted and I were batting about with great authority. And now that I needed a new model, fate stepped in.

I strolled around the back yard with camera, tripod, and so on, but all the neighbors stayed indoors and I was forced to go out front and look for strangers. An urchin of five or six came trudging along the sidewalk with a businesslike air, dragging a noisy burlap sack, and asked, "Any old bottles?" as he drew abreast me.

"You in business for yourself?" I asked. He said he was, that his name was Pete and he lived up the street, and he asked if what I was holding was a camera.

"Yes," I said, and beckoned him around to the back yard. "I have a business proposition to make," I said. "Our basement is a treasure trove of old bottles. Let me take a few pictures of you and I'll give you all the bottles you can drag."

"Let's see the bottles," he said, "and can I have some of the pictures?"

"Three prints," I said. I seated him on the back-porch steps, set up the camera, and focused.

"How about the bottles?" he said.

"Hold still," I said from under the black cloth, and took a picture. "Now turn around and pretend you're looking at something, to make it more interesting," I told him, getting ready to take another.

"I could be looking at those bottles," said Pete. "That'd be interesting."

"Okay, okay," I said, and we went to the basement and harvested a grocery carton of old bottles. Pete arranged himself on the back-porch steps with them, and as soon as I ducked under my cloth and looked through the ground glass I was glad he had been persistent; the composition was now more interesting. I took a couple more pictures and then heard the lad yelling, "Hey, Annie," and when I came out from under the cloth he was luring another model toward the steps. It was a tiny Negro girl, dressed to kill. I had never seen her around there before. "Who's she?" I asked Pete, and he said merely that she was Mrs. Somebody's cleaning woman's baby who came along sometimes.

He seated her on the step beside him, first dumping his original bottles out of the sack and gallantly arranging the sack on the steps for her to sit on, to save her finery. Then he held a soda bottle up in the air and I got a marvelous shot of both the children looking up through the green glass. There was magic in their faces, and I began to realize that Pete had more picture sense in a minute than I had in a month. I would have used up the rest of my plates on them had not the little girl's mother come squawking out of a house two doors away, searching for her. She whisked Annie off, muttering, and Pete resacked his bottles and left. I told him it would be a week before his pictures were ready, to keep him off my back, but I developed the plates that night and made prints the next night, and even my wife was impressed. She had started coming to the darkroom to keep Ted and me company, and when she saw the picture of the children looking through the bottle, she said, "This one is good enough to win a prize. Let's enter it." She was referring to a contest the St. Louis *Globe-Democrat* was then running for amateur photographers. "And let's not say anything to Dad," she added. "Let's surprise him."

Ted agreed. "Sharp as a tack," he said, examining the print with a magnifying glass. "You can count the kids' eyelashes. Nice genre shot."

So I entered the picture in the newspaper contest, titling it: "Back-Porch Pastime," and when I gave Pete his prints I omitted that one. I may have had a feeling it was against the contest rules to hand out prints of an entry; I do know that I had begun to have a few twinges about the picture; it was so clear and full of detail, and I hadn't realized Pete was so smudgy from his bottle hunt and had looked quite a bit like a boy trashman as he posed. I wondered what his parents were like and if his father could take a joke. But presently I reflected that there must be hundreds of pictures entered in the contest and that I would very likely lose, so I cheered up. I had never won a contest in my life, and when three weeks passed without incident, I felt a sense of pleasant regret, like a man who has been turned down by a beautiful girl he couldn't afford to marry anyway.

But on Sunday of the fourth week, all without warning, it happened. Father chanced to see it first. He was eating Sunday breakfast and leafing through the magazine section of the Sunday *Globe-Democrat,* when he let go of a piece of coffeecake and it dropped into his coffee, producing quite a fountain. He sprang to his feet to avoid the splash, upsetting his chair. It was not unusual for him to drop things into his coffee when he became absorbed in the newspaper, so none of us paid much attention until he started shaking the magazine section and making choking sounds. He thrust the section toward me. "Is this—is this——" he cried and could not finish.

I had a look. There, blaring out in sepia ink at me, was my photograph of Pete and Annie, prize winner in the Human

Interest Class, so it said, with my name in boldface type. "Is it mine?" I said. "Yes. I was going to tell you I'd entered it, but then we——"

He shook his head. "I mean, is this——" He swallowed, looked hard at the picture again, and shuddered. "It says: 'Ba—Ba—Back-Porch Pastime.'"

"That's what I called it. You had to have a title——"

He shook his head hard. "Back porch?" he croaked. "*My* back porch?"

"Why, sure," I said. "That's where I took it. With your camera."

Father clapped one hand to his forehead. "Oh, God," he said. "And with my own camera. And your *name's* on it. And the address. Kenneth, how could you do this to me?"

Pat, Ted, and I looked at each other in bewilderment. "We thought you'd be tickled to death, Dad," Pat said with a tinge of reproach. "It had to be a pretty good picture to win. And look how sharp all the details are——"

"Ow-w-w," Father moaned. "Details!" He shook the paper some more, as if choking somebody. "It makes the place look like a damn shanty. How did these old bottles get all over my nice back steps? And that old sack? And these two colored children sitting——"

"Only one was colored," I said. "The other just looks that way. And they were both very nice kids. Very co-operative."

"Co-operative," he said bitterly. "It's humiliating. Thousands of people will see it. Millions. I just hope none of my friends notice the thing and think this junk yard is where I——" He was interrupted by the telephone's ringing. The call was for him, and he picked up the phone with a look of foreboding.

"Oh, hello, Gus," he said to the caller, an old friend he saw occasionally. He listened for a few moments, looking somewhat haggard and swallowing several times. Then he seemed suddenly to come to a big decision. Squaring his shoulders, he turned so that his back was toward us, and

KEN KRAFT, WINNER OF FIRST PRIZE...........

toward me in particular, and spoke into the telephone, loud and clear: "Yes, I happened to see that thing in today's newspaper, too, Gus," he said, "but they made some kind of a fool mistake. I don't know *who* that Ken Kraft is."

There was a pause, broken only by my outraged breathing. Father had often disapproved of me, but up to this moment he had never disowned me. "Well, you know newspapers," I heard him tell his friend. "They got the address mixed up too. There certainly isn't anything around here that looks like anything in *that* picture."

He hung up and marched out of the room without finishing his breakfast and without looking me in the eye as I glowered at him. "Doesn't know who this Ken Kraft is," I said to my wife and brother. "What am I—a figment?" Pat tossed her head.

"Address mixed up," Ted said. "A likely story. And what's the matter with having a few old bottles around anyway?"

Father probably heard us, for we did not speak softly, but he didn't answer. He was prowling around the back porch, presumably to make sure there were no old bottles or young children cluttering it up, and when he left for church, he stayed away all day to miss telephone calls from friends.

Curiously, coming after this, I had no trouble with Pete's family at all. They were charmed to see their son burst into the public eye, and when Pete told me of this a day or two later, I dropped by his house to identify myself. I made them several prints of the winning picture and told them that when my father had seen it in the newspaper he had particularly remarked on their nice little boy.

# 18.   *Father and Culture*

Father was not a bookish man. If the public library had
blown up, it would not have inconvenienced him for a minute. At rare intervals someone had given him a novel for a
gift, probably as a desperate last resort, but the few books
he had bought for himself were all intended to quicken his
wits so he could make more money. He seemed the last man
likely to join a book club. Yet this is what he did at this point
in our stay with him. My wife and brother agreed with me
that it made no sense at all, and it was some while before
we realized what Father was really up to.

The book club he joined was one we had never heard of,
but it was no slouch at marketing its wares. It fired a book
and a pound or so of leaflets at Father by return mail when
he answered an ad, and two more books hit him while he
was still reading the first one. He screwed a stronger bulb
into his chairside lamp and began to read faster.

By the time he finished No. 1, he was four books behind
but he was picking up speed, and he took a fast few moments
between books to recommend the first one to Pat, Ted, and

me. Following his photo-contest uproar he had become contrite in a stiff-necked way, but we had not wholly forgiven him and he was plainly uncomfortable about it. He had stopped talking to us about photography—and, indeed, could hardly make out what we were saying, we had grown so technical. He seemed stuck at dead center, a general without an army.

He rocketed off on his second book, now and then glancing hastily at the living-room clock to see how many pages he was doing per hour. The next club selection caught him before he was quite finished, in spite of all, and he added it to the pile on the small table beside his chair. In his orderly way he was stacking the books in the sequence of arrival, as if they were chapters in a story. At the rate the stack was growing, it was becoming almost dangerous to sit in Father's chair.

It may occur to someone at this point to wonder why he did not cut off the flow of books until he had time to catch up. For surely there was a way to do this? Yes, the book club had provided a way, though not as easy a way as the better-known clubs provided. Father could return new books within a certain number of days in lieu of paying for them. It took some doing but it could be done, and finally Ted asked him about it. To Ted, Father was a constant horrible example of extravagance, and it depressed him to think he was making all manner of undeserving people wealthy. "I'm going to read them," Father told him. "That's why I didn't send them back."

"It isn't very hard to send them back," Ted said. "Use the wrapper they come in, see, and paste a new address label——"

"Yes, yes," Father said. "I know all about that."

"I'll even do it for you," Ted said. "All you'll have to do is pay the postage."

"Dammit," Father said, "I don't want to send them back. I want to keep them."

"*All* of them?" Ted said after a startled moment.

"They're books, aren't they?" Father demanded. "This is something I've been meaning to do for a long time—read more books."

Ted made a final try. "If it's books you want, I know some good secondhand bookstores downtown on Pine where you can buy all kinds of books for a dime each. How about it?"

"Ha," said Father, curling his lip. He patted the stack on his little table. "Not these kinds of books. These are the latest things in culture, son."

A great light dawned on Ted at these words, and he hunted up Pat and me. We were playing a game of darts. "Guess what?" he said. "Dad's reading those books for his head bone." He looked at our vacant faces. "For culture," he said.

"*Those* books?" Pat and I said together.

"He's turned into a culture vulture," Ted said.

We had not looked closely at Father's books, but they seemed the sort recommended for light summer reading. He had called the first one a powerful novel of modern life, a phrase that rang so strangely on his tongue, we had no doubt he was quoting the club publicity. We decided to have a harder look at the stack and did so when Father had gone to bed that evening after reading like mad for two and one-half hours. He had had to push back his bedtime by fifteen minutes in the effort to keep from being utterly swamped.

"Well, I guess it depends on what kind of culture you mean," Pat said after we had leafed through some of the books. "This one's called *Leap Lightly, Lover,* and it seems to deal with modern manners, in the broad sense."

I was fingering a tome titled *One-Horse Junction,* and I had the same impression. "Sort of a racy sociology," I said.

"This one runs more to anatomy," Ted said, surveying a bosomy creature on one of the dust jackets. "Hot ziggety."

At any rate, it was Father's time and money, and if he wanted to collect frothy fiction it was his privilege. Knowing Father, we should have known he would not stop there. He

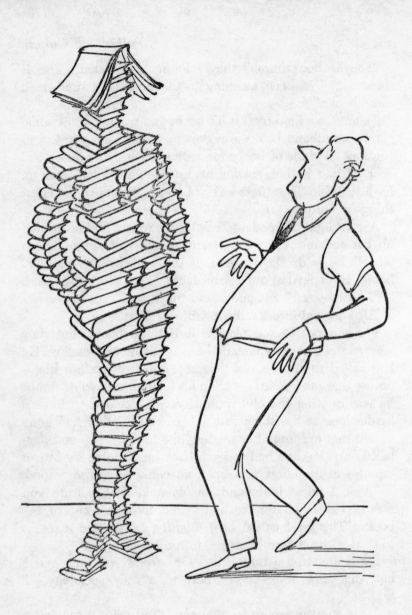

was incapable of stopping there. His true role was not that of culture seeker but of culture bestower, and it was some more of his recent dogged bad luck that he had got hold of the wrong culture to bestow.

He began to press the campaign hard when he had finished his third book, usually urging his literature on us while we were at the dinner table, a captive audience. "I'm getting a lot out of reading these books," he said. "Very educational." We chewed along on our dinners, clods indifferent to education. "A person has to keep up with things, you know," he said. "Keep alert." This sounded to us like another quotation from the book club's promotional material. "The brain," he said in a reproving, paternal tone, "doesn't stand still, you know. Reading books keeps it growing." This was, we were positive, right from the club horse's mouth.

As dinner-table discourse this soon became wearing. "Oh hell," I said privately to Pat, "let's read the things if that's what it takes to keep him quiet. Ted probably can't spare the time from his studies, but you and I can skim through a few, anyway."

We each got one of the books Father had finished reading and pointedly set to, delighting him. Though generous in lending, Father had no mind to see his growing library nibbled away by borrowers with poor memories, and to this end he had got himself a rubber stamp. On the inside covers of each book appeared in purple ink the information: PROPERTY OF E. O. KRAFT. It also sprang from the margin of every tenth or so page, as though a house detective had his eye on the reader and expected the worst.

My wife, who could read much faster than I, was half through her book by the time Father had left us for bed. "Say," she said to me then, "what's yours like?" She looked startled.

"Well, I'm only to the third chapter," I said, "but things are picking up. We've had bits of masochism, and I'm beginning to think the heroine's son is also her nephew."

"Let's trade," she said. "I'm not sure what this one's all about, but if it's about what I think it's about, I've got better things to do with my time."

We swapped books and read awhile. "Yep," I said. "It's about what you think it's about if you think it's about sex."

"How's that?" Ted said, coming upon us on his way to the refrigerator after studying. I explained and said we realized he was too busy to read the books. "I'm not that busy," he said, and dived in.

Presently Pat laid aside her serving of culture. "I simply can't understand Dad," she said. "You know how strait-laced he is. And yet he's been reading these things and trying to get us to read them."

"Well, I think I understand it," I said, "although you may not believe me. Dad doesn't know what they're talking about."

"Listen," she said, "if *I* know what they're talking about, anybody knows."

I shook my head. "He knows what incest is, for instance, but he doesn't think anybody writes about it in a book."

"Sure, that's right," Ted said.

Pat looked at us. "You mean he never—I mean, you're his sons, after all. Didn't he ever—well—speak to you about . . . things?"

"We never discussed them," I said. "He felt that the way to teach a boy the facts of life was to feed him three times a day and keep him busy mowing the lawn."

"That's right," Ted said. "It's lucky I decided to be a doctor or I might never have found out."

"Well, then, I think you'd better talk to Dad," Pat said to me.

"Oh, come now. If you expect me to tell him about the birds and bees——"

"About these *books*," she said. "Somebody has to. We don't want people laughing behind his back, do we?"

"Guess you're right," I said. "I'll see what I can do."

I didn't have much hope of convincing Father his book club was selling him erotica for culture, and I wondered even how to go about it. He was Victorian-prim on such a touchy subject and would turn red from the insteps up, and bolt, if I said one wrong word. I waited till the next evening when he was getting home and met him at the garage. "About those club books," I said, and he smiled and nodded. "Mighty fine books," he said. "You'll get a lot out of them."

"To tell you the truth," I said, "I'm getting a little more out of them than I expected." He looked mildly baffled. "Don't misunderstand," I said. "I'm not objecting to their publication. I'm against censorship in any form."

He looked quite a bit baffled. "Censorship?" he snapped. "What are you talking about?"

"Some of those books are pretty frank."

"Nonsense," he said testily. "I've read them and I didn't see anything wrong. I'm going to loan them to some of the fellows at the office, those I can trust to bring them back."

I saw I'd have to haul out the only big gun I could hit him with. "Now, listen, Dad," I said, lowering my voice, "I know you don't run into the seamy sides of life, working at a respectable office and all, but I have. When I was a newspaper reporter there wasn't a day that I didn't run into dozens of scandals and deviations." This was a terrific exaggeration, but I thought it justified.

"I can't believe there's anything like *that* in my books," Father said after a moment, but his voice was husky and the steel of conviction was gone. He walked into the house frowning and looked uneasily at Pat. That evening his reading pace slowed to a crawl. He did no more than four pages, though I think he read them over twenty times trying to trap an erotic reference.

Unfortunately for his purpose he was as unsophisticated as a brownie, and he slurred right over the juicy bits without knowing it. He would have died before he asked me to point out in the books what I was talking about, but the doubt now flourishing in his mind was enough. He had lost

his confidence in culture and he wanted no more club se-
lections. He stowed the books already on hand in the upper
shelf section of his secretary-desk and locked the glass doors.
Then he wrote a stern letter to the club, telling them to cease
and desist in their mailings to him.

He reckoned without the intricacies of the system. A fresh
selection came slamming in even before his letter could have
reached the club headquarters. Father sent it back without
opening it. This happened again, and then he got a bill for
both books. He returned the bill with another letter referring
to his first letter and commanding the club to strike his name
from its rolls. In a few days he got another dun, and while
he was thinking up a fierce reply the newest club selection
arrived.

"Let me handle 'em," Ted said, for the sake of Father's
blood pressure. "Friend of mine got on a necktie-by-mail
sucker list, and instead of sending them back he sent the
company a stiff bill for storage. Stopped them cold." But
Father could not bring himself to do this. In his world businessmen were decent citizens no matter how much they
disagreed, and decent citizens do not keep goods without
paying for them. He sent the latest book back, unopened,
and wrote another blistering letter.

He received and sent back three or four more books and
wrote as many outraged letters during the next month or
two, and then the books suddenly seemed to stop coming.
Father assumed he had finally pounded some sense into the

club's head, but I had a feeling Ted had something to do with it. I had noticed some zippy-looking new novels tossed into one of his desk drawers, and there were a few mysterious gaps in the bookshelves downstairs where there had been some faded volumes of Emerson's essays and a limp-leather copy of *The Little Minister*.

When I mentioned this to Ted, he gazed at the ceiling awhile and then said vaguely that he wouldn't be surprised if the book-club bookkeeper had grown discouraged with certain return-mailing mistakes of Father's and had finally whacked him off the culture list.

# 19. *Gathering of the Clan*

With the collapse of his culture campaign Father's stock as
the hero of his household had dropped practically out of
sight. It had never been very high except in his own mind.
Now even he could no longer close his eyes to his miserable
status as a father-image, and undoubtedly it was this that
made him so reckless about joining in a proposed reunion
of his family on his mother's side and exhibiting his young.
Ordinarily he wouldn't have touched such a shindig. He was
not allergic to his relatives or anything, but he felt no need
to see most of them in between funerals, where everybody
caught up on the news.

The relative who dreamed up the reunion was one of his
cousins, Emmaline, a sweet, imposingly figured woman who
belonged to the only branch of the family tree that had
blossomed out with money. Emmaline's father had done well
in business, so that the family had had servants and other
nice things all their lives. Emmaline's reasons for wishing a
roundup of the rest of us ragtag and bobtail were obscure,
perhaps even to herself. She simply picked a certain Sunday

and started telephoning around to see how much chicken salad and iced tea to figure on. When she got to Father on her list, he said yes, he'd come and bring the three of us, and then he had to break the news to us.

"There's going to be a reunion kind of thing up at Emmaline's," he said. He seemed to be speaking mostly to me, so I looked him in the eye and waited. "Your aunt Emmaline," he said. "You know." She was not my aunt but it was handy to call her that, and she was the right age for an aunt, a contemporary of Father's.

"All right," I said. "Give Aunt Emmaline my best regards if you see her." I knew Aunt Emmaline but just barely and would have had trouble recognizing her on the street.

"She's the rich one, isn't she?" Ted said.

Father looked impatient. "That's none of my business," he said. "Yours either. The thing is, she's asked us to come to this get-together." He glanced defensively about. "And I told her we would," he said, and braced himself.

"I think that's very nice of her," Pat said.

"Okay with you?" I asked Ted.

He shrugged. "What's the news from Flat River?" he said. It was the gag line from some current joke, a sort of shaggy-dog joke, and it meant "yes."

"What?" Father said, staring at him. Father wasn't much of a hand at jokes. He forgot them as soon as he heard them, and he had no use at all for shaggy-dog jokes. In fact, they made him mad.

"Ted means he'll go to this rooty-toot of Aunt Emmaline's," I said. "We'll all go. When is it?"

"Sunday," Father said after swallowing his amazement at how agreeable we were being.

"Tell me something about these relatives of yours," Pat said to me afterward, "so I'll know what to expect."

I couldn't tell her much. My mother's family had been a large one—there were six sisters and two brothers—and there had never seemed to be much visiting time left over for Father's side of the house beyond his sisters, Lizzie and Dean.

"I remember a smooth green lawn and a two-story brick house with a veranda," I said, "and a uniformed chauffeur driving a tall, black Packard limousine up the driveway. I think I was about four years old."

"That's the last time you saw them?" Pat cried. "Not since you were four?"

"I've run into some of them here and there. They struck me pretty favorably. I hardly feel as if I'm related to them."

"Are any of them around our age?" she wanted to know.

"Some," I said. "One, anyway."

"A girl?" she asked hopefully.

I shook my head. "Fellow named Ludwig. Kind of a brain. He's a sort of cousin and I haven't ever actually met him, but Father used to hit me over the head with his record when my grades at school were down. I grew to hate old Ludwig."

"You hated one of them and didn't know any of them. This is shaping up into quite a family party. I wouldn't miss it for anything."

In the interval before Aunt Emmaline's party Father seemed to be having second thoughts about agreeing to go. Apparently he had started off thinking the massing of his family might add to his stature and have a good effect on us, but now he had begun wondering what effect we were going to have on the family.

About Pat he had no qualms, but he wasn't so sure of Ted and me, and at length his uneasiness settled on a target. He began to listen when we told each other jokes. I noticed him doing so as Ted was telling me the one about the fellow on a blind double date whose girl had so enormous a nose that it drove him to drink, and the more he drank, the more he stared at the poor creature's nose, until finally he demanded to know if she smelled anything dead around there. Flustered, she said no, she didn't smell anything dead around there. Why? "Because," said her date in ringing tones, "if *you* don't smell anything dead around here, there can't *be* anything dead around here!"

"What's funny about *that?*" Father demanded. Ted and I were weak from laughing. "I think he was a smart aleck."

"Sure, he was a smart aleck," Ted gasped, "but he was a funny smart aleck, Dad."

"I'll tell you what he needed," Father said. "He needed a punch in *his* nose."

Ted and I looked at him for a few minutes. He usually didn't even listen to our jokes. "Well, maybe the girl slapped him," Ted said gently.

Father returned to his newspaper and then suddenly looked back at us. "Listen," he said, "don't go telling anything like that at your aunt Emmaline's party."

Ted and I exchanged blank glances. "You don't think that's a *dirty* joke?" I said to Father.

He grew rigid in his chair and a flush colored his neck. "I hope I raised you better than that," he barked, and plunged back into his newspaper.

"Do you know what he's talking about?" Ted asked me when we had left the room.

"Maybe some of our relatives have big noses. Maybe he thinks they might take it personally."

"Okay, that's reasonable," Ted said. "I don't want to hurt anybody's feelings." We agreed not to tell the big-nose joke at the family reunion, especially if we noticed any big noses, but the following day Father threw us a curve.

"Heard about this fellow," I asked Ted, "who saw the big crowd staring up into the sky?" I saw that Father had come to attention.

"No," Ted said. "What about the big crowd staring up into the sky?"

"That's what puzzled this man. So then he noticed that one of them was a fellow he knew, and he stepped up to him and whispered, 'Hey, Pete—what's everybody looking at?' And Pete kept right on staring up into the sky, and he whispered back, 'Not a darn thing—but, boy, have I got the world by the tail since I got this stiff neck!'"

Ted busted out laughing, and Father gave him a baffled look. Pat, who could take our jokes or leave them alone, sighed. Father frowned at me. "I don't get it," he said.

"He had a stiff neck," I said, pantomiming it. "That's why he was holding his head up." Father continued to eye me. "He wasn't really looking at anything special," I said, "but you know how people are. If they see somebody looking hard at something——"

"I know, I know," Father snapped. "But I don't call that much of a joke."

"Well, that isn't the joke," I said. "The joke is the way he took it."

Father's eyes did not leave my face. He had green eyes, and when he was under stress, glints of topaz showed up. His eyes were now practically polka dot as he studied me. "The way he took it?" he repeated slowly. "*That's* the joke?"

"Sure, it's the joke," Ted put in. "The guy was such an optimist about his stiff neck."

"He was a *nut*," Father said flatly. "I've *had* stiff necks." He started to stalk from the room. "I'll appreciate it if you forget all about jokes like that before the party Sunday," he said to me, pausing momentarily on his way out.

Ted and I regarded each other. "It must be something else," I said at last. "It can't be that the whole damn family has stiff necks."

"If you mean why he doesn't want you to tell any of your famous jokes at the family reunion," Pat said, "it's perfectly plain. He doesn't want you to disgrace him."

"Disgrace him!" Ted and I exclaimed together.

"Listen," she said. "He knows his relatives' sense of humor better than you do. He's nervous. He doesn't want them to put you down for a couple of morons alongside that genius Ludwig you were talking about."

"Aha," I said. "Ludwig. I'll bet that's it. And I thought I'd got him off my back when I finished school."

"What kin is he?" Ted asked. "Our second cousin?"

"Third," I said, "I think. Anyway, far enough removed to have an I.Q. of 153, as I recall it."

"Good Lord," Ted said.

"Oh well, maybe he'll be home sick in bed Sunday," I said. "A virus may be going around by then."

For the good of Father's nerves Ted and I agreed with a suggestion of Pat's that we expose him to no more of our jokes before the family reunion. Ted and I were beginning to be sorry we'd said we would go, but Pat now wanted to meet Ludwig. She said she didn't know many smart people and might get something out of it. Father seemed to be calming down a bit. And then on the very eve of the reunion Pat and I shook him all up again.

It was entirely innocent on our part. All we did was to buy an automobile. We had been looking around for a good trade on a used car and weren't in any hurry, but a salesman friend popped up with an offer of a convertible sedan for our car and $400, and we grabbed it. The convertible was a shiny black Packard 120 with a white top and black leather upholstery, and it looked as long as an ocean liner and felt springy and wonderful. We drove home in it with the breeze ruffling our hair and with little boys whistling at us as we passed, and as I steered the sleek beauty up our tricky driveway, Father was in the back yard, smoking his pipe and practicing croquet shots. He stared, and blinked, and stared. "I don't think he knows it's us," Pat said, and waved. "Yoo hoo, Dad," she cried. "Lookit our new car."

A kind of shudder ran through Father, and something plopped to the ground. "There goes his pipestem," I said, and we stepped out.

"Is that really y-y-*yours?*" Father said numbly, jabbing a finger at our gaud.

"Just got it," I said. "Pretty, huh?"

Father's eyes were riddled with dots. "Ho—ho—holy cow,"

he muttered in a hoarse voice. Over a period of years he had worked up from Fords and Chevrolets to Buicks, and there he had stayed, buying the smallest size Buick every two or three years and never dreaming of anything bigger or fancier. If he had wanted a Packard or Cadillac he could have afforded one—and a new one, rather than the used cars my own income required—but he didn't want one. He admired them from afar, as rich men's cars. Owning one simply didn't occur to him. He didn't feel that rich.

"Well, why not?" I said. I had none of his inhibitions here. "And what a sweet thing to handle. Want to try it?" I held out the ignition key, and he backed off as if it was hot.

Ted came bounding downstairs, having spotted us from the window, and raced around the low-slung dazzle, crying that it was about time somebody had a gorgeous thing he could borrow. Father looked at him bleakly and back to Pat and me as he prepared to get himself out of the presence. "That thing gives the wrong impression," he said heavily. "If you run into somebody, they'll think you're a millionaire and sue you."

"Do you know what it cost?" I said. He waited. "Our old car and four hundred dollars." His jaw dropped slightly. I suppose he was thinking vaguely in terms of thousands.

"Well," he said after a while, "that isn't quite as much as I thought. But it *looks* . . ." His eyes roved uneasily along the streamlines of the long, glossy car. The white top was folded neatly back; the leather of the seats gleamed softly, and the brightwork was climaxed by a silvery symbol on the apex of the radiator. Father's shoulders sagged at the spurious show of wealth. "It *still* gives the wrong——" he began, and shot a sudden startled look at me. "You're not planning to drive this to the party tomorrow?" he cried. "*Are* you?"

"Sure," I said. "We'll give 'em a treat. Want to ride with us?"

He did not answer. For the time being I really think he had lost the power of speech.

Sunday afternoon when we drove to Aunt Emmaline's family reunion Ted deserted Father to ride with Pat and me in the dream boat, which we had spent the morning polishing until it hurt the eyes to see it. To be frank about it, the car's looks were its strongest point, but it certainly did have the looks. Since I wasn't real sure where in north St. Louis Aunt Emmaline lived, Father led the way in his bourgeois sedan, sitting low in the seat, his hat jammed unusually far down on his head, as Pat, Ted, and I rolled grandly along behind him, waving now and then to admiring pedestrians, and sounding our clarion horn at those too fascinated with us to move out of harm's way.

I was surprised to find that Aunt Emmaline's house was not the mansion of the visit in my childhood. It was a substantial, typically good residence of a better-class north-side neighborhood, but it was not grand. I parked in a nice prominent place in front, and Father selected a spot up the street so far removed from us that we had to wait on the sidewalk while he hiked back. Then we made an en masse entry, and Ted and I immediately found, as we had thought, that we knew hardly anybody.

There were twenty-six of us milling about the back yard, shaking hands and saying what a fine idea this was, wasn't it? We had almost made the rounds, and Father was wearing a less hunted look than he had arrived with, when one of my new girl cousins came loping around the corner of the house with her eyes wide. *"Come see what's out front,"* she bleated. "A *great* big enormous gorgeous con*vert*ible." In the moment of interested silence that followed I could see the knot of Father's tie jumping up and down as he swallowed, and his face looked greenish.

There was a kind of surge through the side yard to the front one, to behold the wonder, and Father and his brood were swept along as on a tide. Our kinfolk halted out front and drew in their breaths sharply. "Emmaline," somebody finally managed, "do you mean to say that somebody in *this* neighborhood drives a car like that?"

Aunt Emmaline was as confounded as the others. "Mercy, no," she cried. "It certainly doesn't belong around *here*."

"In that case, and since it's parked here," said a male voice with a cool twang of utter logic in it, "it must belong to someone among us." No one had to tell me who had spoken. I hadn't met him yet, but it had to be Cousin Ludwig.

I cleared my throat. "As a matter of fact, it's our car," I said. "Pat's and mine. We just bought it." The silence that followed was impressive. All eyes shifted toward us, including my rich aunt Emmaline's very startled blue ones, and it was at that precise instant, I think, I suddenly understood that my rich relatives had never been really rich—just in very comfortable circumstances for a time, by all appearances. And intuitively I saw something else—that from this day for-

ward, and to my father's secret dismay, *his* branch of the family would be known as the rich one and be expected to act accordingly.

Father's voice, husky with embarrassment, abruptly blurted out for all to hear. "All it cost them," he declared fervently, "was four hundred dollars and their other car." It did him no good, as anyone could see. Our other car, everyone was plainly thinking, must have been worth a fortune on the trade-in.

Slowly we drifted back again to the back yard, where a trestle table had been set up to hold a buffet dinner as soon

as Aunt Emmaline could pull herself together and get it there. As Pat left to give her a hand, Ludwig nabbed me. We needed no introduction. We seemed to know each other by instinct. Taller and a little older than I, Ludwig had intense black eyes behind thick lenses and a Lincolnesque rawbonedness. His big feet were shod in stout, police-type shoes, and he shook hands like a gorilla catching hold of a live wire. I noticed Father eying us from across the lawn, chewing his lip. Ted stepped up beside me to meet his cousin and did not stand on formality. "H'ya, Ludwig," he said. "How do you like my brother's loud new car?"

Evidently the remark struck Ludwig as humorous. He threw back his head and opened his mouth—a large one—and emitted a bray that stood our hair on end. He had the most tremendous laugh I had run into in years. As it bounded off neighboring walls, I saw that Father was looking appalled, as if his worst fears had come to pass and that now Ted and I were telling Ludwig jokes. I thought of stepping over and reassuring him; he had gone through about enough today, it seemed to me. But I was detained by Ludwig.

"Speaking of loud cars," he said, still blowing and gasping, "have you heard the joke about the absent-minded fellow who was tacking down the wall-to-wall carpet?"

Ted and I stared at Ludwig and then at each other. And then we started to smile. "No," we said as one man, "we haven't heard the joke about the absent-minded fellow tacking down the wall-to-wall carpet. What is it?"

Ludwig stopped to chortle to himself as a warm-up. "Well," he said, "he was almost finished tacking it down when his wife pointed to a bump in the middle of the rug and shrieked, 'You fool! The cat's under there. Don't you ever notice *anything?*'" Ludwig paused to tear off a few more chuckles. "So the fellow stopped tacking," he said, "and started tearing the rug loose to get this yowling cat out, and then he said mildly, 'Well, I did notice that it seemed to be an unusually noisy rug.'" Ludwig exploded in so powerful a blast of merriment that I glanced at Aunt Emmaline's rear

windows to see if any were shattering. They weren't, but
from across the lawn I saw that Father was looking fairly
shattered.

I smiled at him and waved, and he closed his eyes as if
in pain and looked away. I really thought he might have
shown more faith, but I felt I knew now how to finish his
day of reunion on a sort of upbeat and incidentally square
an old account of my own.

I took Ludwig by the arm and started steering him across
the sward. "I want you to tell that joke to my father, Cousin
Ludwig," I said. "And if you know any more good ones, tell
him those too. You never saw a man like my father for ap-
preciating jokes."

## 20. *Father Is Stricken*

The beautiful autumn of the Midwest was well under way
when I took my girl aside for a serious chat. It seemed to
me that the time was close upon us to decide how much
longer we were going to go on living under my father's roof.
Ted was increasingly busy at medical school and would be
cutting ties with home more and more, which removed one
big reason for our having moved in with him and Father.
Also, I felt we owed it to each other to re-establish our own
household. As to Father, I had no doubt he would adapt himself to a change like a cat. In fact I had a notion he would
welcome it, and I couldn't blame him. He had hatched this
household to be a benevolent autocracy, and it had turned
into a wild-eyed democracy. His victories had been few and
paltry, his frustrations legion. He could issue commands,
but they were very likely to plop on the empty air. He could
demand our admiration or our sympathy, and if we weren't
too busy we might spare him a few moments. What did he
have to lose by losing us?

"And there's another reason, too," I told Pat. "So far it's

only a rumor, but there may be some changes coming at my office. I may step into a better job here if the grapevine's right about somebody going to New York. In that case we'll be better able to afford a nice home, and we'll probably want to do some of the entertaining it isn't so easy to do here." I didn't have to explain that one. Father kept his usual early bedtime hours whenever we had guests, and it put a damper on the parties to speak in undertones and tiptoe about downstairs.

"Well, this is going to take some planning," Pat said. "House hunting, and proper timing, and separating our things from Dad's things, and I don't know what all."

The first thing to do, we agreed, was to take a long, hard look at real estate, and so the next Saturday and Sunday we began it. There was nothing very unusual about our looking at houses—we often did so, since we would eventually be in the market for one again—and for the nonce we put off telling Father that this time we were serious. Perhaps we thought it would upset him. As it turned out, he was the one who did the upsetting.

We came home late one Saturday afternoon, tender in the feet from real estate, and found the house dark. Yet Father's car was in the garage. "Maybe he went out for a walk," Pat said, and then noticed his hat on the kitchen table. This was most unusual. He always put his hat in his hall closet. A noise came from the living room and we hurried in there and lighted a lamp. Father was stretched on the sofa at the south end of the room. His eyes were closed.

"He's just asleep," I said. "That must have been a snore we heard."

At the sound of my voice Father's eyes opened slightly. I thought they wandered a little, trying to focus, and it struck me that his color was poor. He swung his legs to the floor and came to a sitting position on the sofa, but he didn't get up right away. He sat there swaying a bit from the hips, and

Pat caught her breath. "Dad—you're sick," she exclaimed. "What's the matter?"

He looked bewildered. "Nothing, nothing," he mumbled. "I'll be all right in a minute. You can go ahead with dinner." He leaned forward, holding his head in his hands, and after a few moments we withdrew to the kitchen.

"What do you think?" Pat asked me in a whisper.

"I think I'll fix him a drink," I said after giving it some thought. "When in doubt——"

"*I* think he'd be a lot better off in bed. Did you see his face?"

I said I had, but so far as bed was concerned— "He's never been sick in bed a day in his life. Literally. I'm afraid it would scare him if we suggested it."

The door that led from the kitchen to the short hall where the stairway led up to the second floor was open, and suddenly Father appeared there, leaning against the walls as he walked. "I think I'll go to bed," he said carefully. "I'm not very hungry." We started toward him, but he shook his head. "A good night's sleep," he said, going up the steps. "That's all I need."

We listened until we heard him safely upstairs, and then Pat prepared to act. "I think we ought to call a doctor," she said. "At least we ought to call Ted." Ted was doing some medical stint, but I knew how Father would feel about our calling a doctor. Considering his lifelong admiration for doctors, he had surprisingly little to do with them. This is not to say he was continually well. As a matter of fact, he had a rich store of symptoms, and whenever he felt ill he sorted out the symptoms of the moment with the alert interest of a connoisseur. He then diagnosed his trouble and prescribed for it. In this way he had seen himself safely through countless attacks of heartburn, bronchitis, risings in the head, feebleness, and internal tumult. He was strictly an internal-medicine man and his medicine chest was so extensive it overflowed from the bathroom cabinet above the washbasin into the big bathroom closet, which it monopolized. A good many of these drugs were given him by doctors of chemistry at his office, being free samples sent them by manufacturers who foolishly thought they were doctors of medicine. Others were the products of Father's company. They offered so wide a choice of cures that once a guest for luncheon who developed a bit of indigestion and was offered the use of Father's medical storehouse found seven separate remedies for what he had and got over it before he could decide which one to patronize.

After Father had been upstairs awhile I went up and listened at his bedroom door. My report quieted Pat somewhat. "I think he's fallen asleep," I told her. "I can hear heavy breathing. He seems a little restless, but I think we can postpone calling the doctor and see how he is in the morning." By morning, I felt sure, Father would be ill in his normal way; that is, he'd be sick as a dog and in full command of dosing himself back to health. But this was no ordinary illness. If we needed further proof of this we had it the next morning when Father failed to get out of bed at six o'clock, or at seven, or even at eight.

Now and then Pat or I tapped on his bedroom door to see if there was anything he wanted done. He sounded no worse than he had the day before, nor any better. "Where's Ted?" he said at last, looking restively toward Ted's unused bed. I told him Ted had stayed at the hospital for the night but we expected him home shortly. "Just tell him I'm taking it easy," Father said. "Just for today." I wondered at his tone. He sounded as uneasy as if the doctor was coming.

Pat, though, would have nothing to do with any deception. "Dad's sick," she said as soon as Ted arrived. "Sick in bed and he won't let us *do* anything."

"Umph," Ted said in a professional manner, and stamped upstairs to Father's bedroom. "What's the matter with *you?*" we heard him saying.

"I just felt a little under the weather," Father replied. "That's all. I'm getting along all right."

"Why are you in bed then?" Ted said.

"I'm just taking it easy," Father said, raising his voice. "Just being sensible, dammit."

"He's sounding better already," I said to Pat as we eavesdropped. "At this rate Ted's going to make a marvelous doctor."

"Well, keep on being sensible," Ted said, starting to leave the room.

"I look all right, don't I?" Father asked.

"If I were you I'd see a doctor," Ted said. We could hear Father swearing to himself as Ted returned downstairs.

Pat studied his face. "Shall we call Dad's doctor right away?" she asked. "I've got his number right by the telephone."

"*I'd* want a doctor," Ted said, "but you know how he is." We told him of finding Father ill the day before, and so on, and he decided we could mark time for a while and keep an eye on the patient. "Try a little tea and toast on him," he said.

Pat made it and took a tray up. "Whazzis?" Father said. She told him. He waved languidly at the chair beside his bed, and she set the tray there, urging him to try to eat, and mentioning that Ted had recommended it. He did not reply, and when she picked up the tray later he had merely nibbled at the toast and sipped a little tea. Ted said this was not strange, but it was my wife's belief that the situation was desperate when a man lost his appetite.

She took counsel with herself. "I'd try him on asparagus," she said, "but it's out of season." Father liked asparagus, and since he knew somebody whose doctor had said it was good for him, Father reasoned it was good for him too. He also ate celery because he understood it was excellent for the nerves. "But there's not much nourishment in celery," Pat murmured. She peered into the kitchen pantry. "Hm-m," she said, coming out with a canister. It was something called Mate, pronounced "mah-tay." It came from South America and you made a hot drink with it, and where on earth Father got it I didn't know. He had brought it home one day, announcing that in South America native burden bearers used it to give them strength. "And that's just what he needs—strength," Pat said, and rapidly brewed a potful of the Mate.

She hurried a cup of it up to Father, this time with some crackers on the tray. "What is that—soup?" he muttered.

"Mate, Dad. For strength," she said.

Evidently in his illness he had forgotten about bringing home the Mate. "Mah what?" he croaked.

"It's from South America," she said. "All the native burden bearers drink it."

He smelled it and made a face. "They can have it," he mumbled, and lay back on the pillow with his face averted.

Ted tasted the Mate when Pat brought it back downstairs and said he didn't blame Father. He said he thought that if Father became scared about his illness he'd ask for the doctor, and we agreed that while this kept everybody on edge, it was probably the way we'd have to play it. During the day Pat plied him with various taste thrills such as tapioca pudding, beef broth, fruit juices, and would have tried calf's-foot jelly and sassafras tea if she had had any, but his appetite remained fugitive. He stayed in bed except for an occasional shuffle to the bathroom, where he was dabbling among his vast store of germ killers. "And I wish he wouldn't," Pat said. She seemed to be regarding Father as a grown-up boy with a chemistry set that might produce an explosive mixture. "It's all right for him to dose himself if he isn't sick," she said, "but when he is, I don't think he ought to take any chances."

But by the next day something began to take effect, or perhaps Father's constitution was bigger than his medicine. He remained in bed but he felt like eating a little something. Not much, but something. Delighted with this progress, Pat labored at concocting dishes to tempt an invalid appetite, and she or Sarah Plim bore them upstairs from time to time. This was the order of things for the next few days, with an occasional call to me at my office, asking that I pick up something special for Father's tray at Union Market or some gourmet shop. My wife discovered in herself a talent for nursing, and besides helping carry trays, Sarah obliged by not playing the piano when she dusted. Ted looked in on Father whenever he was home, and they conversed mainly in grunts. We were not now so concerned about calling the doctor unless Father should take a sudden turn for the worse. And as far as we could see, he was improving—except for one puzzling thing: he remained in bed. He was sitting up

in bed most of the day, but he didn't get up and get dressed, as I would have expected, and lie around downstairs, half sick and half cured.

"If he didn't get up at all, I'd think his legs were gone," I said to Pat. "I can't make him out. Before this, nobody could have told me anything could have kept him in bed a week—to say nothing of keeping him away from the office."

It was, actually, the first time in his life Father had missed a day's work aside from vacations. His secretary had phoned on the first Monday, in fluttery alarm, and Pat had relayed a few instructions. Father was remarkably calm about his situation. He appeared to have resigned himself to mending at a snail's pace. I installed a radio at his bedside, at his request, and a good light to read by, and browsed newsstands for magazines I thought he would enjoy. In between listening and reading he pasted Eagle stamps from Famous-Barr into blank books and occasionally answered some real-estate ad that caught his eye, for he was always ready to dicker a little.

Ted made a kind of table for his tray out of an old box, so the tray wouldn't slide down his legs. This proved a great convenience, and Father thought up another one himself. He got from one of his bureau drawers a little tinkle bell so that he could summon Pat and Sarah upstairs without yelling himself hoarse. The bell had a carrying sound—once I heard it when I was on my way home and still half a block from the house, but I should add that a window was partly open in the bedroom; Father was ringing for someone to come lower it an inch or two. Occasionally he rang when he wanted someone to climb up and chat with him.

In between these trips Pat and Sarah tore upstairs on their own once or twice a day when they heard Father getting out of bed, in order to change the sheets. Pat had heard somewhere that fresh sheets were a morale builder for the sick, and she was using some lavender-scented ones for an extra boost. Before the first week of Father's indisposition was over, she found she had slimmed down by three pounds, and Sarah remarked in passing that there were exactly seventeen steps in the stairway to the second floor, two of them with loose rubber treads you had to watch like a hawk, and that she was asking Saint Expedite to lend his influence toward Father's restoration.

At this stage of things Pat, Ted, and I took counsel again on the situation. I said I thought Father was looking a good deal better. "And his appetite's returned," Pat said. "You could say it's normal." We looked at Ted for a professional opinion.

"I'm not a doctor yet," he said, "but speaking as a son, Dad looks practically well to me, except for one thing." He hesitated. "You've known him longer than I have," he said to me. "Have you ever known him to stay in bed if he didn't have to?"

I shook my head. "Not even when he was sick and would have been better off——" I was interrupted by the tinkle of Father's bell from upstairs. Pat rose and left, like a fire horse at the gong. She returned in a few moments and addressed Ted and me a little breathlessly. "What was the name of that mayor of St. Louis who said, 'We got a moon yet, ain't it?' when the street lights went off?" she asked.

Ted and I stared at her. "For God's sake, why?" I said.

"He wants to know," she said, as if impatient at my question. "He says he got to thinking about it and he can't remember the name."

"Tell him I'll check it downtown tomorrow at the library," I said. "They know everything." She went back to tell him, and Ted and I listened to her feet pattering up the seventeen steps once more. "Have you thought about what specialty you might go into, Ted?" I said. He said he thought it was too early to decide. We could hear Pat walking around upstairs on some new mission for Father. "Psychiatry," I said. "I was just now thinking of psychiatry. I believe there's a big untapped field there."

Sunday came and passed, the second in succession that Father had spent in bed, and on Monday I received a startling piece of news. I saved it to tell Pat when I got home from work and she had taken Father's dinner tray up and we were alone downstairs at our own dinner with Ted's plate in the oven to stay warm for whenever he got there.

"Remember about somebody from the office going to New York?" I said. "Well, the rumor was right. They confirmed it today."

"Who is it?" she said. "Anybody I know?"

"You might say so," I said. "It's me."

Our dinner that night did us very little good. I can't remember even eating it, though I guess we did, because part way through it we were interrupted by Father's bell. I took the call—he wanted his reading light shifted a trifle and the electric heat pad brought to put on his shoulder—and I fixed him up and carried his dinner tray back downstairs.

"I almost told him," I said to Pat. "It was on the tip of my tongue for a moment."

She bit her lip. "Now what do we do? About Dad, I mean?"

Actually I hadn't formally accepted the New York assignment yet. But this was just corporate courtesy, to give me a chance to talk to my wife first. But I hadn't told them my father was flat on his back. "He wouldn't stand in our way, of course," I said to Pat.

"And that's just the trouble," she exclaimed. "He'd insist we go. But how can we desert him now, with things the way they are?"

"There's only one thing I know to do," I said. "The time has come when we have to get the facts. We'll just have to call in Dad's doctor, and we'll have to do it without telling him we're going to, I guess."

At about this point in our conversation Ted got home and we told him the news of our New York offer. He saw at once that with this we had all abruptly arrived at a major turning point, that this household had now run its course, and he agreed that for Father's own sake we had to know the state of his health. In the midst of our conference Father's bell tinkled imperiously and we all jumped. Pat sped upstairs to do for him, and I telephoned Dr. Raggler.

"Been sick over a week," the doctor growled at me, "and you're just now calling me?"

"You know how he is, Doctor," I said. "Of course, if he'd seemed real bad——"

"I'll be over in a little while," he said. "Keep him in bed."

"Oh, he's no trouble to keep in bed," I said. "In fact, that's what's bothering us."

Pat came downstairs and I told her the doctor would be over pretty soon. "This evening?" she cried. She started back upstairs again at a run. "To straighten up the bedroom," she hastily whispered back to me, and flew off as if the doctor was coming to diagnose the housekeeping.

"Does he suspect anything?" I asked her when she returned.

She shook her head. "He seems quite happy and peaceful. Just the way he's been for the past week."

The doorbell rang, and she went, praising herself for being so forehanded now that the doctor was arriving so quickly. But when she opened the door it wasn't the doctor. It was the rector at Father's church. Somehow it hadn't occurred to any of us that Mr. Lightfoot would call, yet it was perfectly natural. Father had missed church for two Sundays running; something had to be wrong.

Since Father was ready to receive visitors whether he knew it or not, we hustled Mr. Lightfoot upstairs at once so as to get him out of the way before the doctor came, but I suppose we should have given Father a little warning. He had heard the doorbell, but he wasn't expecting spiritual help. When Mr. Lightfoot loomed up in the bedroom doorway, the patient gave a start that almost yanked the covers off. Mr. Lightfoot took a seat beside the bed on a chair I got him, and Father, his shoulders swaddled in an old sweater, was trying to look like a senior warden as we left them alone.

"Good heavens," Pat said as we filed downstairs to the living room. "*Now* here's the doctor coming up the front steps." Through the glazed entry we could see old Dr. Raggler, black bag in hand, clumping up the front steps, looking impatient with an ailing world as always, and intending to take no nonsense, and we opened the door in a hurry so he wouldn't have to waste time ringing the bell.

"Where is he?" the doctor said, walking in. "Upstairs?"

"Yes," I said, "but the minister's with him at the moment."

"Suffering cats," said the doctor, making for the stairway. "Why you waited till now to call me——"

"He isn't here to administer the last rites or anything," I said quickly. "He just dropped by to say hello." But I was talking to Dr. Raggler's heavy, stooped back as it went up the stair well. In another moment there was an explosive sound from Father's bedroom. "How did you get in here?" we heard Father demanding sternly.

"No thanks to you," his old friend snapped. "What in holy hell you been doing to yourself, Ed?" Downstairs we cringed, and after a brief pause we heard Father again.

"Dr. Raggler, Reverend Lightfoot," he announced.

"How do, Reverend," the doctor said briskly. "All right, Ed—let's have a look at you. Get that damn fool sweater off."

Mr. Lightfoot came downstairs in a matter of seconds and walked solemnly to the door. "Dr. Raggler is an old friend of Father's," I explained. Mr. Lightfoot looked earnestly at his hat. "What I mean is," I said, "he's——" I was interrupted by the doctor's voice howling at Father to shut up for God's sake while he listened to his heart. "I mean, he's an old friend," I murmured, and shook hands with Mr. Lightfoot as he departed.

Pat, Ted, and I waited in the living room. We were not eavesdropping, but to not overhear some of Dr. Raggler's remarks we would have had to leave the house, if not the neighborhood. Still, they didn't tell us much until the doctor had finished his examination. ". . . Did you a world of good to get away from your desk awhile, you old fraud," we heard him saying. Downstairs we looked uncertainly at each other. Was there a note of too deliberate casualness in his voice? Dr. Raggler was never known for subtlety, but . . .

He came thumping downstairs and we all stood up. "Ha. Hmph," he said, glancing at us under his eyebrows. He had been the attending physician when I was born and when Ted was. I wondered if he knew that now we were grown and that we had to know the truth.

"How is he, Dr. Raggler?" I said. "Because if it's serious, we'll have to——"

He suddenly jerked a thumb at the ceiling as if we could see through it at Father. "Sound as a dollar," he said flatly. "I wish *I* could stay in bed a week and be waited on hand and foot." Perhaps we looked nonplused, because he grinned then and added with a shrug: "Oh, he had a strange bug right at first, maybe, but after the first two or three days . . ." He walked to the door and then turned and looked at the three of us hard. "You know," he said in his best public-address tones, "it's pretty nice to have the children fetching

and carrying for you—even if you have to stay in bed to be boss."

He left without more ado, and after another moment to collect our thoughts we all went upstairs, our footsteps firm.

The door to Father's bedroom was wide-open, and he was sitting in bed holding a newspaper as if reading. He glanced uneasily around at the three of us, and his face was in the light from his bed lamp, and it was as red as if he had a high fever. But he didn't have a fever.

"How are you feeling, Dad?" I asked.

"Doc says I'm all right now," he said stiffly. Pat adjusted the sweater around his shoulders, and he looked as if he wished she wouldn't. "I'm all right," he said again. "I'm going to get up and go to the office tomorrow."

"I guess we'd better tell you the news now, then, Dad," Pat said. "There won't be any time in the morning if you're going to the office."

He sat up in bed a little straighter.

"The company wants to send me to New York," I said. "If I take it, Pat and I will be leaving pretty soon. Less than a month."

"*If* you take it?" Father cried. "You're not thinking of turning it *down?*"

"They just told me today," I said. "It's a good promotion, of course."

Father snorted, and his whole bed vibrated. "How many other men have they sent to New York in the past year?" None, I told him. "In the last five years?" he demanded. They had sent none I knew of, from my department. He folded his arms and nodded, a short, complacent nod. "That's what I thought. Chip off the old block. Of *course* you're going to take it."

"You—you don't mind, Dad?" Pat asked. "I mean about this ending our arrangements here, and all—our household here?"

"Mind?" Father cried. "Certainly I don't mind," he said heartily, and then caught himself. "Well, yes, I do mind," he amended. "I'll miss you something fierce. You bet I'll mind, a whole lot."

For the moment he believed it, I think. I'm sure he wanted to believe it. I'm quite sure he would have been mortified to hear what I was hearing. For unless my ears were very wrong, Father's voice was subtly changing. It was changing to the guardedly excited voice of the experimenter whose experiment is suddenly about to turn out amazingly well after all, by ending.

## Wilmington Public Library
### Wilmington, N. C.

---

### RULES

1.  Books marked 7 days may be kept one week.
Books marked 14 days, two weeks.  The latter
may be renewed, if more than 6 months old.

2.  A fine of two cents a day will be charged
on each book which is not returned according to
above rule.  No book will be issued to any person having a fine of 25 cents or over.

3.  A charge of ten cents will be made for
mutilated plastic jackets.  All injuries to books
beyond reasonable wear and all losses shall be
made good to the satisfaction of the Librarian.

4.  Each borrower is held responsible for all
books drawn on his card and for all fines accru-
ing on the same.